Guide

to the

Night Sky

PHILIPPE HENAREJOS

Original edition:
© LOSANGE – 63400 Chamalières – France

Concept: Christian Dorémus
Editing of the French original edition: Valérie Blanchout, Laurence Borot
DTP: Nathalie Mathonnat, Isabelle Véret
CAD: Christophe Courtier, Véronique Janvier
Graphics, picture research: Jacques Theillard, Anne Guillemain

With the collaboration of the Reader's Digest editorial team

Acknowledgments: Our thanks to François Colas for his kind
assistance.

Original title: *Le Guide d'Observation du Ciel*

Copyright © 2005 for this English edition:
Tandem Verlag GmbH
h.f.ullmann is
an imprint of Tandem Verlag GmbH

Translation from French: Dick Nowell, Clive Unger-Hamilton
Editing and adaptation of the English edition,
typesetting and overall project management:
SMALL PRINT, Cambridge
Project coordination: Alex Morkramer, Nadja Bremse
Cover design: Peter Hynes
Front cover photo (background): © Helga Lade Fotoagentur,
Frankfurt a.M./ photo: Photri

Printed in China

ISBN 978-3-8331-5155-2

10 9 8 7 6 5 4 3 2 1
X IX VIII VII VI V IV III II

www.ullmann-publishing.com

CONTENTS

INTRODUCTION

To look at the sky is to behold the Universe. Even with the naked eye, examples can be seen of all the major classes of heavenly body that make up the universe: several planets, many thousands of stars, a handful of nebulae, and three galaxies. This is enough to start anyone on the discovery of the limitless depths of space. The cosmos begins right here, just a hundred kilometers or so above the Earth's surface, and extends in all directions for thousands of millions of light years. We can journey across space simply by lifting our gaze to the starry sky, pointing a small pair of binoculars at the Milky Way, or turning a basic telescope to the Moon. But, like a real journey, this voyage of the eyes is all the more enjoyable for being properly prepared. Visiting a historic monument is of little interest unless you know something of its history; similarly, observing the night sky really becomes fascinating once you know what you are looking at. "Galaxy," "nebula," and even "star," "planet," "satellite," and "comet," are all terms with precise meanings, referring to different kinds of object. It is worth finding out what they signify. Similarly, the "astronomical unit," the "light year," and the "parsec," words which have the ring of science fiction, are in fact the units of measurement that allow us to get to grips with the size of the universe. So before going outside and looking up at the wonders of the sky, prepare yourself by making a quick imaginary tour of the universe, to learn a little about its composition, structure, and dimensions. This book will be your guide.

A JOURNEY THROUGH THE SOLAR SYSTEM

Our starting point is our observation platform, which we shall be leaving behind only in thought: our Earth. This rocky sphere 12,756 kilometers in diameter is a planet orbiting the Sun once a year (or every 365.242 days, to be precise). It is about 150 million kilometers from the Sun, the star of our daytime. Comparing this distance with the circumference of our planet, which is less than 40,000 kilometers, it

The Earth, our observation platform in the universe, is accompanied in its orbit round the Sun by its only natural satellite, the Moon. This picture was taken by the space probe Galileo. ▷

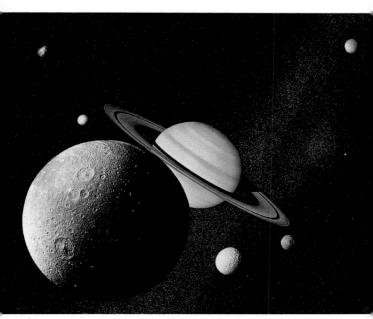

△ *This photographic montage shows Saturn with some of its many satellites:
Dione is in the foreground.*

can be seen that even this first step to the Sun is an enormous one. Distances in space very soon run into mind-numbingly large numbers, so astronomers have decided to call this distance of 150 million kilometers one "astronomical unit," abbreviated "AU." So, saying that the Sun is 150 million kilometers away, or that it is at a distance of 1 AU, comes to the same thing. There are eight other planets orbiting the Sun: Mercury, Venus, Mars, Jupiter, Saturn, Uranus, Neptune, and Pluto. Saturn, to take one example, is 9.54 AU or 1,425 million kilometers from the Sun.

Some of these planets have satellites, less massive bodies that orbit around them. The Moon, a quarter of the size and $1/81$ of the mass of Earth, is our own planet's natural satellite. It takes 29 days to orbit the Earth at an average distance of 380,000 kilometers. Mercury and Venus do not have satellites, but all the other planets do, the larger planets each possessing a great number: Saturn has 18 (not counting the objects that make up the rings), and one of these, Titan, is larger than Mercury. Besides the planets, there are other objects in orbit around the Sun. These include asteroids (also known as "minor planets"), which are rocky bodies ranging from a few meters to hundreds of kilometers across, and comets, which are lumps of ice and dust typically a few kilometers across. All these bodies orbiting the Sun together constitute what we know as the Solar System.

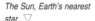

The comets belong to our Solar System. This photograph of Halley's Comet was taken in 1986. ▷

The Sun, Earth's nearest star. ▽

As for the Sun itself, it is quite simply a star. We see it as a disk similar in size to the Moon, but that is only because it is so much closer than all the other stars. If the Sun were as far away as the thousands of stars we see in the night sky, it would be just one more point of light in a perpetually dark sky. The Sun's diameter is 1.4 million kilometers, which means that the Earth would look insignificant beside it. It is a gigantic ball of incandescent gas, which not only produces our daylight, but also enables us to see the Moon and the other planets, as they reflect the Sun's light back to us. This is a fundamental difference between stars and planets: stars produce light, planets do not. To the naked eye, Jupiter, the largest planet in the Solar System, looks just like a bright star: it is too far away to appear as a sphere. But the light it sends us is only reflected sunlight. We might well wonder why it is that, with thousands and millions of stars to light us, the night sky is still dark. The reason is that these other suns, although they produce enormous quantities of light,

Venus

Earth

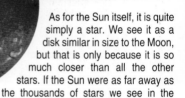

Jupiter

are so far away from Earth that only an infinitesimal proportion of their light reaches us.

Dwarf planet Pluto, which until recently counted as the outermost planet in the Solar System, is some 39 AU distant. Other bodies range further than this (over 100,000 AU in some cases), but they sometimes pass through the inner Solar System, appearing as comets. For distances greater than these, astronomers use different units of measurement, the best known being the light year (ly). This is the distance traveled in one year by light, which crosses empty space at 300,000 kilometers per second. A light year, then, is the equivalent of 63,240 AU or 9.46 million million kilometers, such an enormous distance that it is hard to form any real conception of what it means. An even larger unit of distance is the parsec (pc), which is the distance at which one AU equates to an angular distance of one second of arc. Put simply, one parsec is the equivalent of 3.26 light years (or 206,162 AU!).

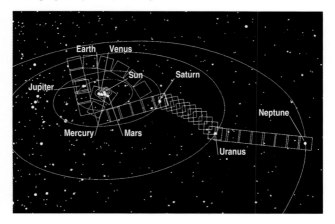

▽ △ *A portrait gallery of the Solar System's planets compiled by the probe Voyager 2 as it passed beyond Neptune. Below are its actual snapshots of the planets, hundreds of millions of kilometers from the probe and already looking like mere points of light; the diagram above shows their positions.*

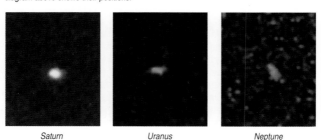

Saturn   *Uranus*   *Neptune*

THE MILKY WAY

The star nearest to the Sun is Proxima Centauri, 4.3 light years away. The brightest star in the sky, however, is Sirius, which from the northern hemisphere can be seen in the evening during winter. Sirius is at a distance of 8.6 light years. This means that, when we look at it, we are in fact seeing it as it was 8.6 years ago, for that is the time it has taken its light to reach us. By comparison, we see our nearest neighbor in space, the Moon, as it was just over one second ago: in other words, it is a little more than

△△ *Artists' impressions of the Milky Way, our Galaxy. It is a group of 100,000 million stars, shaped like a disk, with the stars arranged in spiral arms.*

one light second away. The Sun is about eight light minutes distant, which is of course equivalent to one astronomical unit, or 150 million kilometers. This gives some idea of the enormous gulf that separates the objects in our Solar System from the other stars. Using sophisticated techniques to detect them, astronomers have discovered massive planets, on the same scale as Jupiter, orbiting some of the closer stars: so it turns out that our Solar System is not the only system in which planets are revolving around a star.

Nearly all the stars that can be seen with the unaided eye are within a sphere of 3,000 light years' radius. But the Sun, and its close neighbors visible to the naked eye, belong to a larger group than this: the Galaxy. This is a huge grouping of 100,000 million stars which interact gravitationally. It is shaped like a disk, some 100,000 light years in diameter. Near the disk's center the stars are packed more closely together, forming a kind of nucleus around which the other stars are arranged in what look like spiral arms. The Galactic disk is approximately 10,000 light years thick. There are also stars which are not in the plane of the disk, and these form the spheroidal Galactic halo. This Galaxy of ours is known as the Milky Way. On summer nights, a great milky-white streak can be seen crossing the sky, seeming to divide the vault of heaven into two: this is the concentration of stars in the plane of the Galactic disk, or the "Galactic equator." In ancient times it was called the Via Lactea, and it has given its name to the whole Galaxy.

The Milky Way is particularly clear in summer, because that is the season when the night sky faces toward the Galaxy's center, richer in stars: in fact, we see the diffused light of hundreds of millions of them. In winter the Galactic equator is less marked, because at night we are looking outwards, to where there are fewer stars. We and our Sun are, in fact, some 26,000 light years from the center of the Galactic disk, or about halfway from the center to the edge of one of the spiral arms.

A MERRY-GO-ROUND OF STARS

All the stars of the Milky Way are journeying around the Galactic center, just as the planets are revolving around the Sun. Each has its own orbit, and for the observer this means that the stars' positions are not totally fixed and unchanging. To the naked eye, there is no noticeable change in the sky in the span of a single lifetime: it would take some tens of thousands of years to become apparent that the shape of the Big Dipper (in Ursa Major), for instance, had altered. But even with the basic telescopes used by amateurs, it is possible to observe changes in the position of some stars relative to their neighbors over the course of just a few years. The case of Barnard's Star in the constellation Ophiuchus is particularly striking: it is the fastest-moving star in the sky. Our Sun takes 200 million years to complete its orbit round the center of the Milky Way, which means that it is circling the Galaxy – and carrying us with it – at a rate of 230 kilometers per second.

The Galaxy is home to thousands of millions of suns, but stars are not the only objects it contains. In the space between these bodies are immense clouds of gas and dust: the nebulae. The largest of these are several

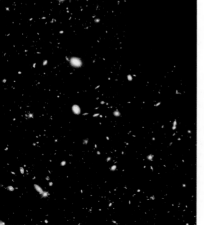

◁ A universe of galaxies. In this picture of a very small part of the sky, taken by the Hubble Space Telescope, only four of the stars in the Milky Way can be seen. All the other objects shown here are galaxies, each containing many thousands of millions of stars.

△ *Our local cluster, the Local Group, includes the Milky Way, M31 (in the center of the photo), and M33 (bottom left).*

hundred light years across. New stars are forming within them, as the gas of which they are composed collapses in on itself. These clouds, although far less dense than the clouds in the Earth's atmosphere, are so large that they nevertheless contain enormous amounts of matter, enough to create new stars of all sizes.

Nebulae where some stars have already formed and started to burn are easier for us to see, since radiation from these young stars makes the nebula's gases shine. The best known of all, in the constellation Orion, can be seen with the naked eye as a whitish patch. There are many such clouds, some of which are completely invisible but act as screens, preventing much of the light from the stars at the Galaxy's center from reaching us. Without these, the Milky Way would be an even more striking feature splashed across the night sky.

Also revolving around the center of the Galaxy are star clusters, each containing up to a million stars, known as "globular clusters." They are between 20,000 and 80,000 light years from the Sun, and many can easily be observed with an amateur telescope. Large numbers of these clusters lie outside the plane of the Galactic disk, so that if we were able

◁ *The galaxy seen here, NGC 891, is several million light years from Earth. All the stars shown in this photograph belong to the Milky Way and are relatively close to us (only a few thousand light years away at most), but NGC 891 is much further away. Between the two lies intergalactic space, completely devoid of stars.*

to look at the Galaxy from one of these, we would see it as an enormous spiral, taking up the whole of the sky.

A MYRIAD OF GALAXIES

For all its 100,000 million stars and its impressive size, the Milky Way is by no means the whole of the universe. It is just one of the numberless galaxies scattered throughout the cosmos. In fact, we may take it that there are as many galaxies in the universe as there are grains of sand on a beach. Some are much larger than the Milky Way, while others are dwarfs: who knows how many suns they contain in all?

The two Magellanic Clouds, visible from the southern hemisphere, are irregularly shaped galaxies 160,000 and 200,000 light years away which orbit the Milky Way. In the northern sky there is another galaxy that can be seen with the naked eye: M31, in the constellation Andromeda. Astronomers consider this a sister galaxy to the Milky Way, since it too is a spiral galaxy and has some 200,000 million stars. At 2.5 million light years away, it is the nearest to us (apart from the Magellanic Clouds, which are satellite galaxies).

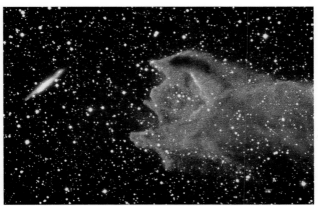

△ An example of just how deep the sky is: the nebula NGC 4, shown here, is a few thousand light years away, while the galaxy that looks just next door to it is in fact tens of millions of light years distant.

Galaxies are distributed throughout the universe in groups called clusters. The three principal galaxies in our cluster, the Local Group, are M31, the Milky Way, and M33. The next nearest cluster, the Virgo Galaxy Cluster, is 40 million light years away. The largest telescopes can see galaxies as distant as several thousand million light years. And this immense space, whose contents we have briefly reviewed here, is accessible to everyone: we only have to look up to see the sky. Probing its secrets, and unraveling its mysteries, can be a fascinating leisure pursuit.

OBSERVING THE NIGHT SKY

THE NAKED EYE OR BINOCULARS

No optical instruments are needed to begin the study of astronomy. A great many useful observations of the night sky can made by the naked eye alone. For thousands of years, astronomers had no other instruments at their disposal, but this limitation did not prevent them from observing the planets, the Milky Way, and mysterious whitish spots in the sky, as well as producing accurate astronomical calendars, predicting eclipses, and calculating the distance from the Earth to the Moon.

GETTING STARTED

Finding a suitable site is the first essential for observers. Choose a place where the horizon is free from obstructions such as trees or buildings, and with as complete a view as possible of the night sky. It is important to avoid pollution from artificial lighting, and town-dwellers will probably have to travel some distance from their urban surroundings. Even in the country, the lights from a small village or a solitary streetlight can effectively wipe out a great number of stars, so a dark environment is required. Secondly, when the Moon is between its first and last quarter, it obliterates the night sky just as effectively as artificial lighting, so a moonless night is best for observation. Finally, allow a good 15 minutes for your eyes to grow used to the darkness, before they can begin to pick out the relatively faint glow from astronomical objects.

WHAT CAN BE SEEN?

The naked eye can discern roughly 6,000 stars. But since it is possible to view only half of the night sky (the other half being underfoot, as it were, obscured by the Earth), around 3,000 are visible at any time. This is plenty to be going on with, however. All these stars belong to the Milky Way: this is our own Galaxy, containing more than 100,000 million stars, and those visible individually to the naked eye are less than 3,000 light years from Earth. On summer nights, a broad pale band extends right across the heavens. This is the main disk of the Milky Way, packed with

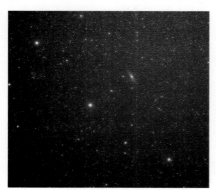

remote stars. Since the Galaxy is disk-shaped and we are within it, we see it as a straight streak across the sky. The eye perceives the light from these countless stars without being able to distinguish them individually.

◁ *The constellation Andromeda, with the galaxy M31.*

16

△ *The constellation Sagittarius, where the Milky Way and the Lagoon Nebula (on the right) are clearly visible to the naked eye.*

Sweeping across this area with the aid of binoculars reveals an astonishing profusion of stars. The constellation Sagittarius contains the Galactic nucleus, some 26,000 light years away, where the density of stars is at its greatest. This is the brightest part of the Milky Way.

A small round blob is visible within this constellation: this is the Lagoon Nebula, 5,000 light years away and one of only two nebulae that can be seen with the naked eye in the northern hemisphere. With binoculars, a small star cluster can also be detected against a pale, misty background. The other nebula visible to the naked eye is M42 in the constellation Orion, observable in late fall and winter. Binoculars reveal the irregular outlines of this immense cloud of gas 1,500 light years away.

The naked eye can also make out several open clusters of hundreds of stars. The most famous of these is the Pleiades, in the constellation Taurus, whose principal stars are easily identified. In the same constellation is the Hyades cluster, which is much more spread out. The Double Cluster in Perseus is clearly visible without artificial aid, but by looking at any of these with binoculars, the viewer will easily distinguish the separate stars. Apart from the Milky Way, only one galaxy is visible to the unaided eye in the northern hemisphere: M31, in the constellation Andromeda. It appears as an oval blob against the dark sky, hardly spectacular to look at, but an incredible 2.5 million light years away.

Finally, the planets in our Solar System are (with the exception of Uranus, Neptune, and Pluto) easy to spot, looking just like stars. Binoculars add nothing to our view of them, except in the case of Jupiter, whose four Galilean moons become visible, and in the case of Saturn, whose largest satellite, Titan, can then be made out.

TELESCOPES

WHAT IS A REFRACTING TELESCOPE?

In the astronomical refracting telescope, light from the object under observation is collected by a large converging lens at the front of the tube, called the objective. From the objective, the rays of light converge to form an image in the focal plane, at the other end of the telescope. A second lens, the eyepiece, is positioned just behind the focal plane to enlarge the image. The eyepiece used will depend on the nature of the object under observation: one with strong magnification for small, brilliant objects such as planets, and weaker magnification for diffuse objects such as nebulae.

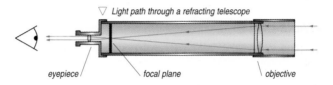

▽ *Light path through a refracting telescope*

eyepiece   *focal plane*   *objective*

THE EARLIEST ASTRONOMICAL INSTRUMENTS

Telescopes are the principal astronomical instruments, although they were at first put only to terrestrial use. Certainly this was the function of the first model, completed in 1608 by the Dutch optician Hans Lippershey. In 1609 Galileo Galilei became the first to find a new role for the instrument by pointing it toward the sky. The telescope at his disposal was hardly more than an inch (30 mm) in diameter and magnified objects to about 30 times their actual size. Accordingly the images were not very bright, and the instrument was not ideally suited to the study of nebulae or star clusters. Altogether, its optical qualities were poor compared to any of the small telescopes that can be purchased by amateur astronomers today, yet its limitations did not prevent Galileo from discovering the phases of Venus, the mountains of the Moon, and Jupiter's satellites.

In 1611 Johannes Kepler established the optical principle of telescopes. In the years that followed, ever larger telescopes (still called "refractors," because their objective lens refracted light rays toward the focal plane) were manufactured. As the diameter of the objective lens increased, the tubes of these instruments also grew to an extraordinary length, the most impressive of them being as much as 38 meters long and consequently extremely difficult to handle. The reason for their enormous size was that the objective, consisting of a single convex lens, produced a strong chromatic aberration: in other words, it split the light from the observed object into the colors of the rainbow, making observation difficult. To cope with this problem, optical engineers ground lenses that were less convex, which in turn necessitated positioning the focal plane further back. It was with instruments of this type that Johannes Hevelius made the first detailed map of the Moon in 1647, and Christiaan Huygens discovered the true nature of Saturn's rings. In 1733 an Englishman, Chester Hall, designed an objective in which a convex lens was attached to a concave one, thereby solving the problem of chromatic aberration.

The late nineteenth century was the Golden Age of refracting telescopes: they produced better images than did reflectors, with their fixed mirrors, and so were used in most observatories. The 40-inch (102 cm) Yerkes telescope in the United States was completed in 1897, and is still the largest refracting instrument in operation. But with this, the limit had been reached: the weight of glass needed for the lenses created technical problems that prevented further development in this direction. Reflecting telescopes came into their own, and have since been continually improved for use in the world's great observatories.

ADVANTAGES

One important feature of a refracting telescope is that it does not go out of alignment. Once the objective lens is in place, nothing (apart from a severe physical shock) can move it. This means that a refractor will survive being transported in a vehicle to sites where weather conditions are most favorable, and gives it a distinct advantage over a reflector (see pp.22–25), though these are increasingly portable nowadays. In recent years it has become possible to produce shorter refracting instruments that are easier to carry, even up to diameters of 5 to 6 inches (125 to 150 mm). This is achieved by using objectives with two or three lenses, allowing the focal length to be reduced while still correcting chromatic aberration. Finally, the image in a refractor is unimpeded: whereas in reflectors the aperture is partially obscured by the secondary mirror mounting, refractors use the entire surface area of the objective lens.

△ *Seventeenth-century refracting telescopes were disproportionately long, to cope with the chromatic aberration produced by an objective with a single lens.*

Telescopes

DISADVANTAGES

Not all refracting telescopes succeed in completely solving the problem of chromatic aberration, so the image of a planet, for example, can appear tinged with blue on one side and red on the other. An objective comprising three lenses is the only satisfactory way of dealing with this difficulty, but most realistically priced refractors use only two lenses. Some of these deal with chromatic aberration relatively successfully, but most are unsatisfactory. The price is the generally the best guide to distinguishing between a good and a mediocre instrument, and it must be added that the chief disadvantage of refracting telescopes is their high price. As far as commercially available telescopes go, it is quite impossible to find a refractor cheaper than a reflector of the same size. The difference in price between the two types is chiefly due to the extra cost of manufacturing and fitting the objective lenses. The cheapest 4-inch (100 mm) refractor of an acceptable standard will cost nearly $1,000, and at that price there are 8-inch (200 mm) reflectors on the market.

MODELS AVAILABLE

At first glance, all refractors look much the same. But although the optical principle is the same in all models, there are still a few points to look out for when choosing an instrument. First of all, avoid instruments with any plastic components, either optical or mechanical. Plastic is sensitive to changes in temperature, which occur frequently during astronomical observations, and an instrument with any plastic parts will be of inferior quality. An adequate 2-inch (50 mm) refractor with no plastic components should cost in the region of $120, and a 2½-inch (60 mm) instrument of similar quality with an altazimuth mounting (see p.26) will probably cost you at least $180.

Secondly, if you need a multipurpose instrument, i.e. one suitable for

△ A 2½-inch (60 mm) refractor suitable for the amateur astronomer.

△ *The 33-inch (83 cm) refractor at Meudon, in France, was the largest in the world when it came into service in 1893. Only the Lick and Yerkes refractors in the USA are larger.*

observing planets in fine detail as well large objects like nebulae, it is important to consider the instrument's focal ratio or *f*-number (the ratio of the objective's focal length to its diameter or aperture). An instrument with a focal ratio lower than 6 is suitable for viewing large groups of stars, comets, nebulae, and galaxies, but obtaining high-magnification images with it will be difficult.

A ratio of between 6 and 8 gives you a multifunctional instrument. Above 8, it will be less well suited to observing galaxies than to detailed study of the planets. In other words, the greater the focal length, the higher the magnification achievable in practice with a telescope of a given aperture. But higher magnification also entails a narrower field of view and a fainter image. This does not matter for planetary observation, since the planets reflect a great deal of light, but it does restrict the viewing of diffuse bodies such as nebulae, galaxies, and comets.

Telescopes

WHAT IS A REFLECTING TELESCOPE?

A reflecting telescope, or reflector, is a telescope which uses a curved primary mirror rather than a lens to collect light from an astronomical object. Rays of light reflected from the mirror converge in the focal plane to form an image, which is viewed though a magnifying eyepiece. Reflectors are built according to several different optical principles, the most widely used being the Newtonian, Cassegrain, and Schmidt–Cassegrain types. The Gregorian reflector is now of historical interest only. The main difference lies in the way in which a secondary mirror is used to divert the light path so that the image is formed at a point convenient for viewing. Reflecting telescopes have the disadvantage that the secondary mirror blocks a little of the incoming light from the object.

THE MOST POWERFUL TELESCOPES

In 1668, Isaac Newton, who had studied the way light splits into a spectrum (particularly when passed through a prism), set about constructing a telescope free from the chromatic aberration that was such a problem with refracting instruments. He used a concave mirror as an objective, rather than a lens; this reflected light rays instead of refracting them, concentrating them on a smaller secondary mirror mounted at an angle of 45° in front of the primary mirror. This means that the focal plane is positioned to the side of the telescope, out of the way of the optical axis. Newton's first model had a lens one inch (25 mm) in diameter and

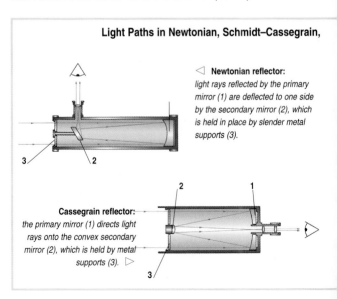

Light Paths in Newtonian, Schmidt–Cassegrain,

◁ **Newtonian reflector:**
light rays reflected by the primary mirror (1) are deflected to one side by the secondary mirror (2), which is held in place by slender metal supports (3).

Cassegrain reflector:
the primary mirror (1) directs light rays onto the convex secondary mirror (2), which is held by metal supports (3). ▷

was only 6 inches (150 mm) long, but it had the magnification of a refractor 60 inches (1.5 m) in length. Unfortunately, the mirrors of the time reflected only about 20% of the light that they collected, which resulted in a much fainter image.

In 1672, Laurent Cassegrain perfected a telescope that worked on a modified principle: the secondary mirror, instead of deflecting the light rays to one side, sent them back towards the primary mirror, through which they passed by way of a central hole. Instead of viewing sideways, the observer could look straight down the tube, as with a refractor. Refractors continued to be preferred for many years, however, because they permitted 90% of the light they collected to reach the eyepiece, whereas the poor quality of the mirrors then available gave a dimmer image. Until the middle of the nineteenth century, nobody believed that reflectors could ever supersede refractors.

In 1845, the Irish peer Lord Rosse built a reflecting telescope nicknamed "the Leviathan of Parsonstown," which was 72 inches (1.8 m) in diameter! It had only 60% reflecting power, but with it he was able to discover the remarkable spiral nebula M51 (which is in fact a galaxy). At the end of that century, giant refractors (Yerkes, Lick, and Meudon) were still the biggest

Cassegrain, and Gregorian Reflectors

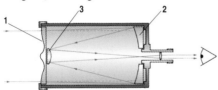

Schmidt–Cassegrain reflector: *light rays pass through a thin lens called a corrector plate (1) and strike the primary mirror (2), from where they are sent back to the secondary mirror (3), fixed to the back of the corrector plate.*

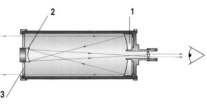

Gregorian reflector: *the principal mirror (1) directs light rays onto a concave secondary mirror (2), which is secured by metal supports (3).* ▷

Telescopes

△ *Lord Rosse's gigantic reflecting telescope, completed in 1845, had a diameter of 72 inches (1.8 m).*

telescopes in the world, but with the entry into service in 1917 of the 100-inch (2.5 m) Mount Wilson telescope in the United States, reflectors finally took the lead. Whereas the glass in a lens over 40 inches (1 m) in diameter deforms under its own weight, a mirror of any size can be constructed without great difficulty, as its whole surface can be supported from behind. With the completion of the 200-inch (5 m) Mount Palomar Telescope in the United States in 1948 and the 6-meter instrument at Zelenchukskaya in Russia in 1975, a new threshold was reached. Their mirrors, weighing several tonnes, posed serious engineering problems. Present-day technology can produce composite mirrors, or single ones that are extremely thin and therefore lighter, while distortion is continually monitored by computer. The largest telescopes currently in use are the two 10-meter Keck Telescopes and the 9.2-meter Hobby–Eberly Telescope.

ADVANTAGES

The chief advantage of a reflecting telescope over a refractor is its lower cost. There are many satisfactory 8-inch (200 mm) models on the market for around $500–$1,500, while a refractor of the same diameter would cost up to ten times as much. Reflectors of acceptable optical quality up to 12 inches (300 mm) in diameter are still affordable. As far as optical performance is concerned, a reflector has the advantage of not producing chromatic aberration in the image. Schmidt–Cassegrain reflectors have the additional benefit of being relatively short, which makes even instruments with a diameter of up to 10 inches (250 mm) relatively easy to handle.

DISADVANTAGES

Reflecting telescopes have open tubes (except Schmidt–Cassegrain models, which are closed by the corrector plate), so moving air currents can arise within them. Another problem is that, over time, the primary and secondary mirrors can shift out of alignment. Both factors reduce the quality of the image, but the mirrors are generally relatively simple to adjust. The secondary mirror inside a reflector's tube not only obscures some of the light entering the telescope; it also diffracts incoming light. This creates diffraction rings around the object, producing an image with less sharp detail than is obtained with a refractor of the same diameter.

MODELS AVAILABLE

The most practical type of reflector is without doubt the Newtonian. A small Newtonian has traditionally been the ideal instrument for beginners, and has allowed many would-be astronomers to make an inexpensive start to their hobby. The smallest generally available is the 4½-inch (115 mm) f/8 model. A 6-inch (150 mm) f/8 Newtonian can be bought for $500 or so, and a 10-inch (250 mm)f/4.5 for around $700. Larger Newtonians tend to be considerably more expensive because of the higher quality of their optical components and mountings, and may also come with integrated software. All reflectors of acceptable quality have a parabolic primary mirror; avoid cheap instruments with a spherical mirror.

△ *The domes of Keck 1 and Keck 2, both telescopes 10 meters in diameter, constructed in the 1990s on the summit of the Mauna Kea volcano, Hawaii.*

MOUNTS AND SETTING UP

TYPES OF TELESCOPE MOUNT

Telescopes need to be mounted in such a way as to allow a view of any part of the sky. The two most common types of mount are the altazimuth and the equatorial mount. The altazimuth mount pivots on both vertical and horizontal axes, enabling the observer to aim the telescope in any direction. The equatorial mount has a polar axis, aligned with the Earth's axis, and a declination axis, at right angles to the polar axis, which carries the telescope. Once an object is in the field of view, it can be tracked across the sky by rotating the telescope about the polar axis only. With the altazimuth mount, a telescope has to be moved about both axes to keep an object in view. In recent years, computerized mounts of both types have become available, permitting the location of a heavenly body by a system of coordinates.

△ The altazimuth mount

THE ALTAZIMUTH MOUNT

Its simplicity of operation (see left) has made the altazimuth mount the most popular with beginners' instruments of 2 to 3 inches (50 to 75 mm) diameter. The observer has to navigate among the stars by sight, as it were, and once the target is in view it will only remain there for a short time because of the Earth's rotation. This movement becomes particularly obvious when observing the Moon with strong magnification: details of the lunar surface pass out of the field of view quite quickly, and the user has to adjust the instrument frequently to compensate for this. However, with only low magnification (up to ×50) the apparent rotation of the stars is not a serious problem, because in this case the field under observation is relatively large and objects take longer to disappear from view. Dobsonian mounts (named after their inventor) are used on large Newtonian reflectors 16 inches (400 mm) or more in diameter, and are a simplified version of the altazimuth mount. The astronomer who chooses a Dobsonian mount will have a substantial instrument, capable of detecting faint objects such as galaxies, star clusters, nebulae, and comets, at an easily affordable price. An altazimuth mount is cheap and simple to set up in comparison to an equatorial mount. It makes the use of high magnification and the accurate location of very faint objects more difficult, but for those who know their way around the heavens, a Dobsonian with a good finder (a small refracting telescope attached to the main one for locating targets) is an ideal gateway to the study of the deep sky.

THE EQUATORIAL MOUNT

There are many kinds of equatorial mount, of which the German is the most popular. This is the type in use on large refractors and most Newtonian reflectors. It is relatively simple to operate, although sighting the instrument at the zenith may occasionally prove difficult. What happens is that, when the tube is pointed straight upwards, it may be obstructed by one of the supports, preventing it from tracking the object under observation. Another popular model is the fork mount. It is commonly used with Cassegrain and Schmidt–Cassegrain reflectors, and is also found on some Newtonians. Sighting at the zenith presents no problem with the fork mount, but it does have another drawback: while almost any telescope can be fitted to a German mounting, a fork mount will only accept tubes up to a certain size. In addition, a fork mount is less rigid than the German type. Other kinds of

△ The German type of equatorial mount

equatorial mount exist, such as horseshoe mounts, but these are not generally commercially available.

Whatever its type, a good equatorial mount – i.e. a steady and responsive one – is worth equipping with a motor drive. This mechanism turns the telescope at the same speed as the apparent motion of the stars across the sky, but in the opposite direction, to compensate for the Earth's rotation. By using a drive, an object can be kept permanently in view without having to readjust the instrument continually, making observation infinitely easier. But accurate initial positioning of the instrument is just as important for effective tracking.

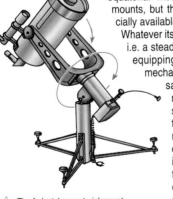

△ The fork-style equatorial mount

SETTING UP A TELESCOPE WITH AN EQUATORIAL MOUNT

In order to operate efficiently, an equatorial mount must be positioned with precision. This setting-up process is an important preliminary to observation, and consists of pointing the mount's polar axis towards the north celestial pole (or towards the south celestial pole, in the southern hemisphere).

An instrument with a German equatorial mount must first of all be standing completely level; if necessary, adjust the length of each leg to

Mounts and Setting Up

How to Locate an Object
with Known Coordinates

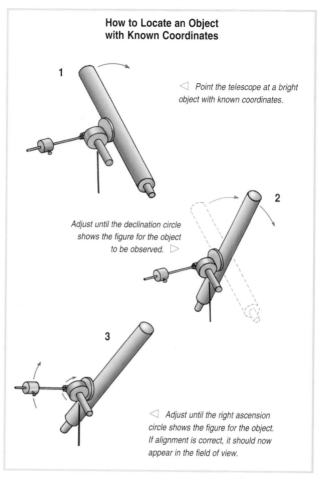

1

◁ Point the telescope at a bright
object with known coordinates.

2

Adjust until the declination circle
shows the figure for the object
to be observed. ▷

3

◁ Adjust until the right ascension
circle shows the figure for the object.
If alignment is correct, it should now
appear in the field of view.

achieve this. A spirit level is often fixed to the mount for this purpose. The angle of the telescope must also be set to correspond to the latitude of your site, using the declination circle (see p.29). Then, point the telescope toward the north celestial pole and, fixing the declination at 90°, use the finder to aim the telescope directly at Polaris (the Pole Star), which is within one degree of true north. When Polaris appears in the field of view, setting-up is complete. Most modern instruments have a built-in polar sight, making it possible to sight Polaris simply by adjusting for your latitude. Setting up a fork-type mounting is done by pointing one branch of the fork towards Polaris, with the telescope set at a declination of 90°.

Polaris appears in the field of view when accurate adjustment is made for your latitude. Perfect alignment is not essential in order to begin viewing the stars, but for time-exposure photography setting-up must be precise. It is not sufficient in this case to point the axis towards Polaris: it must be aimed directly at true north, which may necessitate lengthy adjustments. Once setting-up is complete, observation can begin. It should now be possible to view a star just by knowing its coordinates. The technique is the same whatever the type of equatorial mounting used. First, locate a bright star that you can identify and look up its coordinates (any star atlas will give the coordinates of at least the fifteen brightest stars in the sky). Once these are known, adjust the right ascension circle to the figure for this star. (The setting circles are graduated scales indicating the direction in which the telescope is aimed. The declination circle is fixed, while the right ascension circle may be rotated.) The declination circle should now show the figure for the star's declination. Any slight inaccuracy means that you have not aimed the polar axis of your mount exactly at the celestial pole. Once the right ascension circle has been locked onto the selected bright star, you simply need to maneuver the instrument until both setting circles show the coordinates of the object you want to observe: in theory, it should then appear in the field of view of the eyepiece. On many modern telescopes, setting circles are replaced by electronic controls, but the principle is the same.

If your telescope does not have a motor drive, you will need to make these adjustments as quickly as possible, because the Earth is turning all the time. If adjustment takes more than two minutes, the telescope will end up pointing to one side of the object you are aiming at. With a drive, however, the telescope will follow the rotation of the night sky, and time is not a problem.

◁ *A reasonably priced Newtonian telescope with a Dobsonian mount makes setting-up an easy matter for the amateur.*

EQUIPMENT AND PREPARATION

CHOOSING YOUR TOOLS

The first problem the beginner faces is how to choose the best instrument. If you want to use it for all types of observation (the planets as well as the deep sky), look for an instrument with an f-number (focal length divided by aperture) between 6 and 8. Below 6 the instrument will be more suitable for observing deep-sky objects, while above 8 it will be better suited to high-resolution observation of the planets. Then, once you have decided on the type of instrument you want, the model needs to meet the three essential tests of optical quality, stability, and, to a lesser degree, ease of use.

Optical quality
It is difficult to judge an instrument's optical quality without using it over a period of time. If a reflector comes with an inspection certificate, this offers a guarantee that it meets the standard specified. The degree of optical precision is represented by the Greek letter lambda over a number (λ/16, for example). The larger this number is, the higher will be the quality of the primary mirror, anything below 10 being unacceptable. Refracting telescopes should have at least a double achromatic lens (doublet). The ideal is a lens consisting of three layers (triplet), but the expense of this may prove prohibitive.

A good objective lens is no use if the eyepiece is poor. Huygenian eyepieces (marked H) and Ramsdens (marked R) are of inferior design. They contain only two lenses and give mediocre results, with serious loss of definition in the image obtained. Instruments designed for beginners are often fitted with these. Kellner eyepieces, which have three lenses, are of much higher quality without being substantially more expensive. Orthoscopic and Plössl eyepieces both offer an astonishing improvement in image quality. There are several other types of eyepiece on the market, but these are the most widely available.

Stability
Checking that an instrument is stable is a simple matter. If nothing appears to move or wobble when you shake the instrument gently, that is an excellent sign. But if it seems flimsy or unsteady in any way, either the mount or the tripod is probably not stable enough. This is often the case with

refractors intended for beginners, or f/8 reflectors with wooden tripods. But such instruments are certainly easier on the pocket, and could be suitable for those just embarking on the study of astronomy. If the instrument is to be used permanently in one place, it is worth considering replacing the tripod with a concrete post.

Ease of use

To find out if an instrument is going to be easy to use, check how complicated it is to assemble and to disassemble, and investigate the setting-up procedure. If one person can assemble the telescope single-handed in under 20 minutes, this is reasonable, especially if its aperture is more than 8 inches (200 mm). Bear in mind that, once an instrument's aperture reaches 10 inches (250 mm), its constituent parts (mount, tube, counterweight, and tripod) will be quite heavy. Once the telescope is installed on its mount, setting it up should only take a few minutes. German mounts are fitted with a polar sight, making this a very simple operation.

A good finder is an essential piece of equipment. This small refractor mounted parallel to the telescope tube is of key importance, and if it is of poor quality, it is frustratingly difficult to get worthwhile results, even from a good telescope. Most finders sold with beginners' telescopes are stopped down: the aperture is reduced by a ring-shaped baffle in order to lessen chromatic aberration. As a result, they give an image so dim as to be almost useless. It is better to spend a little more money on an achromatic 6 × 30 finder, which makes it easier to find your way about the night sky. Instruments around 8 inches (200 mm) in diameter often come with excellent 7 or 8 × 50 finders.

There is a wide and growing range of accessories on the market, designed to make operating a telescope easier. Software is available that automatically locates astronomical objects with the help of a database. Telescopes with built-in software can even tell you whether the object selected for observation is actually visible or not! Increasingly, you can make a start in astronomy without having extensive knowledge of the night sky.

◁ It takes about 20 minutes for the eyes to get used to the darkness, before they can make out the details of faint objects.

Equipment and Preparation

PREPARING TO USE THE TELESCOPE

Before you actually set up your telescope under the night sky, it is worth checking a sky atlas to see what will be visible. If you have software that indicates the constellations visible from your location at any particular hour and date, you will know what you can expect to see. In the absence of such software, a map of the sky, whether portable or not, will supply the same information and save a great deal of time outside on what may be a cold night!

△ Avoid using artificial illumination as far as possible, but if it is needed, always use a red light.

TIME TO ADAPT

Having positioned the telescope, you should wait for a few minutes before commencing observation. This is especially important in cold weather, because the inside of the telescope's tube will still be filled with the warm air from indoors. A difference between the external and internal temperatures will give rise to air currents within the tube, resulting in blurred images.

It normally takes 20 to 30 minutes for the temperature to adjust, during which period open-tube telescopes should be left uncovered. Meanwhile, you can set up the instrument and aim it toward the object you want to observe. At the same time, your eyes will be getting used to the darkness; for this reason it is important to avoid using artificial lighting during this period, or even looking at the Moon through the telescope. To show just how important this rule is, try looking for example at the Orion Nebula (M42) after your eyes have been adapting to the darkness for 15 minutes, and then try it again after looking briefly at a bright light. The difference is amazing.

To pick out the fine details of diffuse objects, it is best not to look at them directly, but slightly to one side. You will find that you distinguish features of very faint nebulae and galaxies more clearly in this way, because of the structure of the eye: the rods on the edges of the retina are more sensitive than those in the center.

PRECAUTIONS

In order to avoid switching on a lamp every time you need to change the eyepiece, make sure beforehand that all your equipment is laid out in a precise order. Once this becomes a habit, finding any tool or accessory in the dark is a straightforward matter.

If you do need artificial lighting – to look at a sky map, for example, or to make notes – be sure to use a lamp with a red filter, as this color is the least dazzling to the eye.

You need not take such strict precautions about bright lights when observing the Moon or the planets, as these objects are sufficiently bright in themselves to dazzle an observer. In fact, although this should hardly need saying, when the Moon is between its first and last quarter, its brilliance makes the observation of nebulae or galaxies virtually impossible.

△ Unpack the tube as soon as possible, so that the temperature inside it can adjust to match that of the outside air before you commence observation.

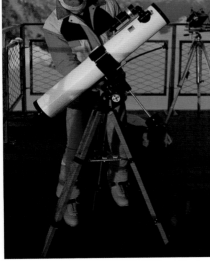

◁ Effective protection against the cold is essential for good observation.

IN THE CITY

In industrialized countries, it is becoming increasingly difficult to find dark places suitable for observing the night sky, and in cities it is necessary to use filters to combat the pollution of artificial lighting. Modern CCD cameras and image processing techniques can also assist in obtaining a clear image. And even if exploration of nebulae and galaxies is difficult or impossible, brighter objects such as the planets and the Moon can still be studied.

SITING AND SETTING UP

To use a telescope in an urban environment, the observer has to find a "niche" in the night sky, an area where nearby buildings or trees do not block out too much of the view. You may need to take your instrument to an open square or park to find an ideal viewpoint.

A south-facing balcony is perfect, of course, for it is in this direction that the Moon and planets pass in the course of the night. Facing east, an observer has to catch heavenly bodies as they rise, while in the west they will be seen on the way down, as they set. The least satisfactory direction is north, for other than Ursa Major (the Big Dipper or Great Bear), Ursa Minor (the Little Dipper or Little Bear), and Polaris, there is less of interest to be seen. Even once a suitable site for the telescope has been chosen, setting up may be a problem if a wall or building blocks the view of Polaris, but this difficulty can be overcome with the help of a compass. Using this, draw a line pointing north on the ground, and then align the telescope along it. All of this assumes that you know the latitude of your site, because the instrument must also be regulated accordingly. This approximate setting-up method is more than adequate for general observation. Since many of the planets are visible to the naked eye, tracking them will present no problem, so long as the

The lights of Paris, reaching further and further out, have rendered the Meudon observatory useless. It used to be in the countryside! ▷

◁ *A view of the light pollution in Europe, which is a serious handicap for astronomers.*

use of strong magnification is avoided. Always remember to take the telescope out of its case a good half hour before starting to use it for observation, to let it adjust to the outdoor temperature and avoid air currents inside the tube causing fogged images. For the same reason, if you are observing through an open window, allow time for the room's temperature to match that of the exterior. In winter this will mean shutting off the central heating.

Finally, in summer, remember that walls and floors that have been exposed to sunshine during the day will continue to radiate warmth after dark, and this heat may cause telescopic images to shimmer. The urban skywatcher will frequently be working in conditions that are less than ideal, and will have to learn how to compensate for these and similar drawbacks.

WHAT THERE IS TO SEE

The Moon, Venus, Mars, Jupiter, and Saturn are the most accessible objects for the city-dweller to observe in a night sky that is never truly dark. If you want to examine their surface in the greatest possible detail, you will need to eliminate all the factors that could impair image quality (as described in the previous section). Once the best possible conditions have been created, the relatively calm atmosphere over cities can offer good viewing. The hours after midnight are usually the best for observation, so long as the weather is suitable.

It is possible to observe double stars even in the city, but locating them can be a problem, as the urban sky offers so few useful landmarks. The Orion Nebula (M42) and the Andromeda Galaxy (M31) are both easy to see, of course, but the very faint regions around their edges will not stand out at all clearly against the rather light city sky, so your view will be hampered by poor contrast. Special filters can help to alleviate this problem, whether it is the nebulae or the planets that you want to observe.

IN THE COUNTRY

The countryside is a far better place from which to observe the night sky. But even here, there is some risk of light pollution. Do not set up close to a road, where the glare of passing headlights will keep dazzling you and interrupting your viewing.

SITING AND SETTING UP

Just like in the city, there are a few precautions to be taken before starting to use a telescope. In summer, do not set up too close to walls or paving that may be emitting heat absorbed during the day; and always unpack the telescope at least 30 minutes before commencing observation. Beyond that, in theory at least, the only limitations are those imposed by the weather or by the telescope itself.

But even in the country, some locations are better than others. Avoid the bottoms of valleys, where layers of air at different temperatures can cause atmospheric disturbance which results in shimmering. Above an altitude of 1,800 meters the air tends to be stiller, although this is not invariably the case. It is precisely this relatively calm atmosphere that has prompted professional astronomers to build observatories on mountain peaks. The well known observatory at the Pic du Midi de Bigorre in southwest France is 2,870 meters above sea level, perched on a mountain top that stands apart from the main Pyrenean chain. In this way, any air disturbance that might be created by other mountains nearby is avoided. It is one of the best sites in the world for astronomy: an amateur telescope up there would produce images of far superior clarity to any it could obtain in the plain below. In addition, the fact that so many stars can be seen with the naked eye from such a site makes it much easier to locate objects for telescopic observation. With the help of a good star atlas, it is possible to locate by eye most of the bodies identified by

The Pic du Midi de Bigorre, in France, is an ideal site for astronomy. The first domes in this observatory were built at the beginning of the twentieth century. ▷

36

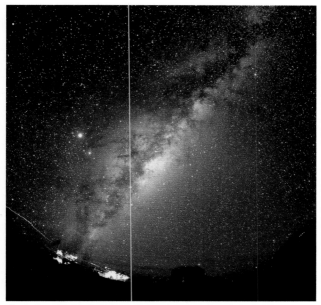

△ *Looking toward the Galactic equator, the sky appears thick with stars.*

Messier, and a good many of those listed in the *New General Catalogue* (NGC) as well.

WHAT THERE IS TO SEE

A good dark night offers limitless possibilities, especially for observing nebulae and galaxies. Atmospheric disturbance, which can impede high-resolution study of the planets or of the Moon, is no serious handicap to the study of such diffuse objects. The most important factor here is the quality of light received, and consequently what can be seen is limited only by the diameter of your telescope.

Even the most tenuous fingers of the Andromeda Galaxy should certainly be detectable, as well as the faintest swirls in the Orion Nebula. And the many galaxies which are too faint to be seen at all in the polluted urban night sky become clearly visible with relatively small telescopes (around 4 inches (100 mm) in diameter).

Finally, with the unaided eye you will also sometimes see artificial satellites passing overhead. They are easily distinguished from airplanes, because their light does not wink (satellites have no navigation lights), and because they generally move much faster: they cross the night sky in around three minutes.

COMET HUNTING

Even without the impressive technical resources which professional astronomers have at their disposal, amateurs continue to make discoveries in the night sky, and comets are probably the most accessible targets for the hunter armed with only modest equipment. With patience and a sound systematic approach to searching the sky, the discovery of a new comet is within the reach of any observer. And when it does happen, the new body is named after its discoverer! On average, about a dozen new comets are discovered each year, half of them by amateurs. Although there is no magic formula that guarantees success, it is worth considering how to weight the chances of success a little in your favor.

CHOOSING A FAVORABLE SITE

Always choose a totally dark place for observation, where the horizon is free from obstruction to east and west. These requirements rule out any chance of searching for comets in or even on the edge of cities. Comets usually appear at an angle of less than 90° to the Sun, so to ensure the best chance of success, search the sky toward the western horizon as night begins, and then around the eastern horizon as it ends.

THE RIGHT EQUIPMENT

The Australian amateur astronomer William Bradfield discovered a comet a few years ago using just an ordinary 7 × 35 pair of binoculars, only capable of producing a fairly low-contrast image. But this was an exception, and a telescope with a large aperture that can capture the faintest of images remains the tool of choice. A 16-inch (400 mm) Dobsonian (a Newtonian reflector with a simple altazimuth mount), for example, would fit the bill perfectly. Just about any decent telescope from the enormous range on today's market will prove suitable for use by comet hunters. A 4-inch (100 mm) instrument will show a comet

◁ Comet Bradfield was discovered with just a pair of 7 × 35 binoculars.

◁ ▽ *A Japanese amateur observer, Yuuji Hyakutake, discovered his famous comet using a well mounted pair of 25 × 150 binoculars, similar to those shown below.*

of magnitude 12, and when the famous Hale–Bopp comet was first identified, it was of magnitude 11. A relatively low-magnification eyepiece is quite sufficient to search the starry background for comets.

HOW TO SEARCH

Whether using binoculars or an astronomical telescope, the technique consists of methodically sweeping the sky in a series of parallel bands, until an unfamiliar object is spotted. This can take hundreds of hours, spread over a number of years. David H. Levy, the great American comet hunter, had no luck for his first 917 hours, which took him nineteen years to complete! Alan Hale and Thomas Bopp, on the other hand, found their comet completely by chance when they were observing something else. However you find it, once a suspect body has been located, you must take great care to confirm that it has not already been identified. It might be a galaxy, a star cluster, or a nebula, for example: a good star atlas will help to avoid any confusion here. It could also turn out to be a known comet which, although faint, has already been tracked for several years by other astronomers.

The best way to check your discovery is to note the object's exact position and see whether it moves among the other stars over a period of one or two hours. If the answer is yes, remember that it could still be an identified asteroid. At this point, stronger magnification may reveal whether the body appears to have a diffuse halo of light around it, confirming that it is a comet.

If the answer is still in the affirmative, apply to have your discovery validated by writing to the Central Bureau of Astronomical Telegrams in the USA. If you turn out to be one of the first two discoverers of a comet, it will be named after you.

NAVIGATING THE SKY

GENERAL SKY CHARTS

THE SKY IN SPRING

This map shows the night sky on April 15 at 22:00 local time for an observer in the northern hemisphere at latitude 45°. For those located further north, Hydra will be very low on the southern horizon, but Andromeda will just appear over the northern horizon.

To use this map, hold it above your head with north pointing toward the northern horizon.

PRINCIPAL CONSTELLATIONS VISIBLE

Hydra, Virgo, Leo, Boötes, Cancer, Gemini, Corona Borealis

WHEN THIS AREA OF THE SKY IS ALSO VISIBLE

May 15 at 20:00
December 15 at 06:00
January 15 at 04:00
February 15 at 02:00
March 15 at 00:00

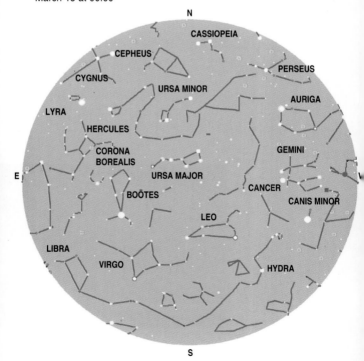

THE SKY IN SUMMER

This map shows the night sky on July 15 at 22:00 local time for an observer in the northern hemisphere at latitude 45°. For those located further north, Scorpius will be partially below the southern horizon, but Auriga will rise higher above the northern horizon.

To use this map, hold it above your head with north pointing toward the northern horizon.

PRINCIPAL CONSTELLATIONS VISIBLE

Sagittarius, Scorpius, Cygnus, Aquila, Lyra, Ophiuchus, Hercules, Corona Borealis, Boötes

WHEN THIS AREA OF THE SKY IS ALSO VISIBLE

August 15 at 20:00
March 15 at 06:00
April 15 at 04:00
May 15 at 02:00
June 15 at 00:00

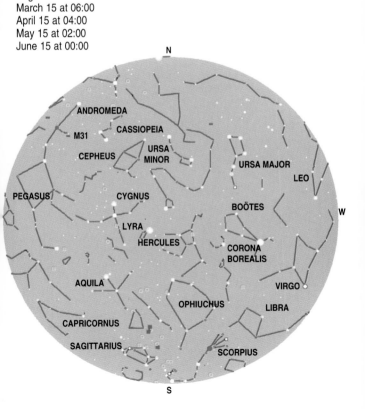

General Sky Charts

THE SKY IN FALL

This map shows the night sky on October 15 at 22:00 local time for an observer in the northern hemisphere at latitude 45°. For those located further north, Sculptor will be partially below the southern horizon, but Ursa Major (the Great Bear) will rise higher above the northern horizon. To use this map, hold it above your head with north pointing toward the northern horizon.

PRINCIPAL CONSTELLATIONS VISIBLE

Cetus, Pegasus, Andromeda, Aries, Sculptor, Aquarius, Delphinus, Pisces, Cygnus, Taurus

WHEN THIS AREA OF THE SKY IS ALSO VISIBLE

November 15 at 20:00
December 15 at 18:00
July 15 at 04:00
August 15 at 02:00
September 15 at 00:00

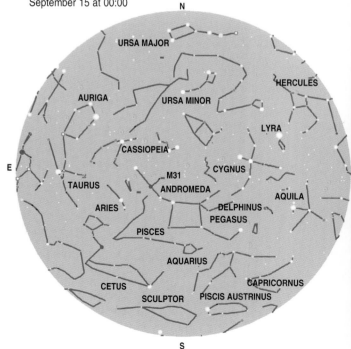

THE SKY IN WINTER

This map shows the night sky on 15 January at 22:00 local time for an observer in the northern hemisphere at latitude 45°. For those located further north, Sirius in Canis Minor will be closer to the southern horizon, but part of Hercules will be visible above the northern horizon.
To use this map, hold it above your head with north pointing toward the northern horizon.

PRINCIPAL CONSTELLATIONS VISIBLE

Canis Major, Orion, Gemini, Taurus, Leo, Aries, Auriga, Cancer, Andromeda

WHEN THIS AREA OF THE SKY IS ALSO VISIBLE

February 15 at 20:00
March 15 at 18:00
October 15 at 04:00
November 15 at 02:00
December 15 at 00:00

OVERVIEW OF THE SKY

THE CONSTELLATIONS

Even a brief glance at the night sky reveals the countless stars that fill the celestial vault, spilling everywhere in confusion. They appear in every color imaginable, and in every shade of brightness. In order to find their way around this vast expanse, the astronomers of Antiquity made associations between groups of the brightest stars and the figures suggested by the patterns they made. These became the constellations, named after the animals or mythological heroes they represented. The constellations Andromeda and Hercules, for example, both date from Antiquity and represent legendary figures.

△ Early maps of the sky were illustrated with beasts and characters from ancient legend, drawn around groups of stars.

Some of these mythological names fell out of use or were changed down the years, while the constellations visible in the southern hemisphere were not identified and named by Europeans until the seventeenth and eighteenth centuries, when the early navigators observed constellations hitherto unknown to them. Still more recently, others have been given the names of scientific instruments such as the Microscope, the Telescope, and the Compass.

As optical instruments became more powerful, the traditional constellations ceased to be sufficiently precise as navigational aids. The number of known stars continued to increase as the limits of visibility were pushed back, and astronomers no longer knew to which constellation the new stars should be assigned. Astronomers from all over the world gathered to redefine the constellations. It was no longer sufficient simply to redraw the celestial figures; instead, the sky was divided into zones bounded by lines defined by coordinates published in 1930. Since then, every point in the sky has been assigned to one of 88 constellations, rather like different countries in the heavens. These new zones maintain their links with the constellations of old, which are contained within them. The modern constellation Orion, for example, is a zone whose boundaries encompass the pattern of the ancient Orion with his legendary belt. A few changes have been necessary: the ancient constellation Argo Navis (Jason's ship), for instance, has been divided into Vela (the Sails), Carina (the Keel), and Puppis (the Stern).

MAPS AND THE REAL SKY

To an observer, the night sky appears as a huge hemisphere with the stars fixed to it. The best artificial representations are to be seen in planetariums, where viewers are positioned beneath a large dome upon which images of the stars are projected. In this book, as in all works on astronomy, the celestial sphere has to be represented by flat maps. Each of the general charts in this section of the book shows the area of the night sky visible to an observer at a specific time. They are shown as circular because they depict the observable sky in its entirety, the perimeter of the circle in each case representing the horizon. The area beyond this, as it were, corresponds to the ground on which the viewer is standing. So the map and all the stars on it represent the entire night sky, like the dome of a planetarium above the head of an observer.

The compass points at the edge of each chart correspond to the cardinal points on the ground. But since an observer's back is to the Earth when

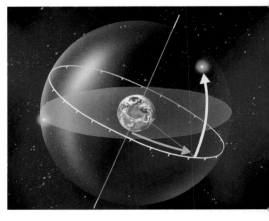

To enable the sky to be represented on a flat chart, all the stars are treated as if they were the same distance away, fixed to an imaginary sphere with the Earth at its center. Coordinates similar to terrestrial longitude and latitude are projected onto the sphere, so that the stars' positions can be precisely defined. ▷

looking upward at the stars, the compass points appear to be the wrong way round. On an ordinary geographical map, north is at the top and south at the bottom, with east and west to the right and left respectively. In the sky, however, everything is the other way round, so that if you look at the constellation Orion, which passes above the southern horizon, the constellation Canis Major appears to the left of Orion, but also to its east! This inversion is reproduced on celestial maps: if you wish to have east on the right-hand side, the map must be turned upside down, but this puts north at the bottom and south at the top. This state of affairs may seem peculiar, but it does in fact correspond to reality. It can be understood by thinking of celestial maps as representations of terrestrial coordinates projected against the sky, just as a person's image in a mirror (a projection against a reflecting surface) is laterally inverted from right to left.

STAR NAMES AND MAGNITUDE

The most obvious way in which the stars differ from one another is in their brightness. Many of the brightest stars were given their names in the Middle Ages, although long before then the ancient Greek astronomer Hipparchus had classified them according to six degrees of brightness, called magnitudes. Magnitude 1 was the brightest, and magnitude 6 represented the faintest stars. This system proved so practical that it has been adopted by modern astronomers, with a few improvements and modifications. Under the best conditions (a clear, dark sky free from light pollution), the unaided eye can see stars as faint as magnitude 6. Beyond that, binoculars or a telescope become necessary. The scale of magnitude being logarithmic, the faintest objects seen with the most powerful

The Fifteen Brightest Stars in the Sky			
Rank	**Star**	**Constellation**	**Magnitude**
1	Sirius	Canis Major	−1.4
2	Canopus	Carina	−0.6
3	Alpha Centauri	Centaurus	−0.3
4	Arcturus	Boötes	−0.1
5	Vega	Lyra	0.0
6	Capella	Auriga	0.1
7	Rigel	Orion	0.2
8	Procyon	Canis Minor	0.4
9	Achernar	Eridanus	0.5
10	Betelgeuse	Orion	0.5
11	Agena	Centaurus	0.6
12	Altair	Aquila	0.8
13	Acrux	Crux	0.8
14	Aldebaran	Taurus	0.9
15	Spica	Virgo	1.0

telescopes (magnitude 29) are 600 million times fainter than those just discernible with the naked eye (magnitude 6).

But names alone are no longer enough to distinguish all the known stars. In 1603, the German astronomer Johann Bayer decided to allocate a letter of the Greek alphabet to each star, usually in descending order of brightness, followed by the Latin name of its constellation (using the genitive case). Aldebaran, for example, the brightest star in the constellation Taurus, becomes α (Alpha) Tauri. Castor is α (Alpha) Geminorum, while Pollux is β (Beta) Geminorum. But because he sometimes assigned letters according to the order of the stars in the pattern, α (Alpha) does not always indicate the brightest star in a constellation. A well known example is in the constellation Ursa Major, where the star ε (Epsilon) is brighter than the one designated α (Alpha). The great star catalog of England's first Astronomer Royal, John Flamsteed, appeared in 1725, six years after its compiler's death. In it he classified every star visible to the naked eye by its position from west to east across each constellation, giving each one an Arabic number. This naming system has been adopted for those stars that did not already have a Greek letter, such as 61 Cygni. Other systems are also in use; for example, the letters R to Z are used in the designation of variable stars.

CATALOGING HEAVENLY OBJECTS

Globular star clusters, open clusters, nebulae, and galaxies are all listed in various catalogs. In the eighteenth century, the French astronomer Charles Messier produced the first list of nebulae (a term which at the time covered star clusters and galaxies as well). He undertook the cataloging of all fixed fuzzy objects because they were interfering with his search for comets. Messier listed 104 objects, giving each a number preceded by the letter M. His catalog is still used today, especially by amateur astronomers. Messier could only observe from the northern hemisphere, so he was of course limited to listing fuzzy objects in the northern sky. The *New General Catalogue*, more comprehensive and designed for professional use, appeared in 1888. In it each object is given a number of up to four digits, preceded by the letters NGC. Together, these two catalogs list most of the objects that can be observed by amateurs.

Coordinates

RA = 6h 45.2m	Dec. = −16° 43′
RA = 6h 24.0m	Dec. = −52° 42′
RA = 14h 39.7m	Dec. = −60° 50′
RA = 14h 15.7m	Dec. = +19° 11′
RA = 18h 36.9m	Dec. = +38° 47′
RA = 5h 16.7m	Dec. = +46° 00′
RA = 5h 14.5m	Dec. = −8° 12′
RA = 7h 39.0m	Dec. = +5° 14′
RA = 1h 37.7m	Dec. = −57° 14′
RA = 5h 55.2m	Dec. = +7° 24′
RA = 14h 3.8m	Dec. = −60° 22′
RA = 19h 50.8m	Dec. = +8° 52′
RA = 12h 26.6m	Dec. = −63° 06′
RA = 4h 35.9m	Dec. = +16° 31′
RA = 13h 25.2m	Dec. = −11° 10′

Overview of the Sky

THE CHANGING SKY

The stars appear to us to be fixed in relation to each other, and over the centuries pictorial representations of the constellations have remained unchanged. In fact they are constantly shifting, though their motion is so infinitesimal as to be imperceptible to the naked eye over several decades. Only very few move enough in the course of a few years for the change to be detectable with the aid of a telescope.

On the other hand, while the stars appear stationary in the sky, the sky itself appears to move. An observer only has to note the position of a star in relation to an object on the ground as night falls, to become aware that a few hours later the sky has shifted to the west. Of course, it is not the sky at all that moves, but the Earth rotating in the opposite direction to the movement observed. It is the same phenomenon that makes the Sun appear to rise in the east each morning and set in the west.

Theoretically, any star should return to exactly the same place after 24 hours. But in reality there is a slight discrepancy between the solar day (the time that passes before the Sun returns to its highest point), which is 24 hours long, and the sidereal day (the time that passes before a star returns to the same point), which is 23 hours, 56 minutes, and 4 seconds. This is because the Earth is orbiting the Sun. It makes one 360° revolution in 365 days, so the Sun appears to move by about 1° per day in relation to the distant stars. As a result, any observed star seems each night to be four minutes ahead of its position the night before. It takes a full year for it to return to its initial position at the identical time. Consequently, as the seasons change, the night sky moves overhead, revealing new constellations as the old ones disappear.

Only those stars in the region of the celestial pole remain visible all year round. All others are subject to periods of visibility, and naturally of invisibility too. As a rule, constellations which are observable before midnight in winter are known as winter constellations, and so each season has its own group of constellations. Orion is one of the best known winter constellations, although from the end of summer it becomes visible toward dawn in northern latitudes.

Remember that the same constellations are observable from one month to the next, though they appear slightly earlier each day, adding up to a two-hour difference over a month. So a star seen in one position at 22:00 on October 1 will appear in the same position at 20:00 on November 1.

Just as the sky changes from one season to the next for an observer remaining in the same place, so it differs from one place to another on the same day and at the same time. Three observers positioned on the same meridian but at different latitudes will each see different areas of the night sky. For example, an observer situated at a latitude of 45° north on a summer night will see the stars that form the tail of the constellation Scorpius brushing the southern horizon. Another, positioned at 30° north at the same time, will be able to see the stars of the constellation Ara, below Scorpius; while a third, at latitude 60° north at the same time, will only see the head of Scorpius rising above the horizon.

The sky as seen simultaneously by three observers on the same meridian at latitudes of 60° (Anchorage/Oslo), 45° (Minneapolis/Turin), and 30° (New Orleans/Cairo) north. ▽

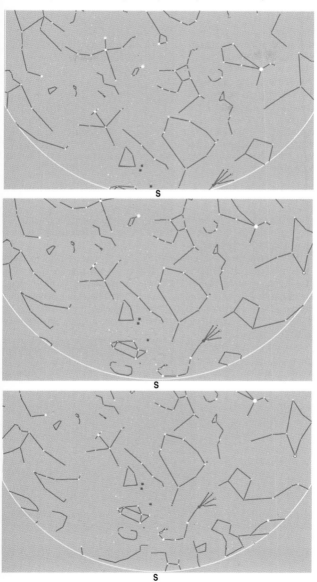

S

S

S

The science of astronomy begins with the unaided eye. Before pointing a telescope at the night sky, it is essential to be able to find your way about. Otherwise, the task of locating a nebula, a galaxy, or even a star bright enough to be seen by the naked eye is quite impossible. On the other hand, once you have learned to recognize the principal constellations, finding other objects in the sky becomes a relatively straightforward matter.

FINDING URSA MAJOR

For an astronomer to be able to rely on a particular landmark in the night sky, as a starting point for navigating among the stars, it must be a feature that is always visible – at all hours of the night and in any season. Ursa Major (the Great Bear) is the key landmark for observers in the northern hemisphere at latitudes of 40° or further north. It is easy to identify from its group of seven principal stars, shaped like an enormous ladle (the Big Dipper or Plough), and it never sinks below the horizon. Its orientation changes according to the season or the time of night, so the Big Dipper can appear the right way up or upside down in the sky.

To find Ursa Major, it is only necessary to look approximately north. If

A photograph showing how Ursa Major and Ursa Minor appear to the naked eye in the night sky. ▷

◁ *A long-exposure photograph reveals the apparent rotation of the sky. The stars describe arcs of a circle around Polaris, which is located almost on the axis of the Earth's rotation.*

you have no idea in which direction north lies, you will have to scan the whole sky, but the distinctive outline of the Big Dipper is easily spotted. The stars of which it is formed are extremely bright, and can even be seen in the light-polluted sky over a large city.

FINDING THE POLE STAR

Once you have found Ursa Major, locating true north is quickly and easily done. Extending the line between its two brightest end stars (Dubhe and Merak) onward by roughly five times its length leads the eye to a fairly

▽ *Ursa Major points the way to Polaris, the north pole star, which marks true north.*

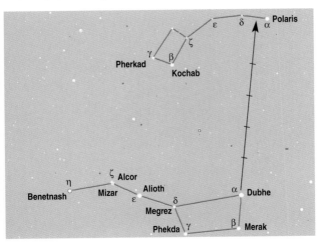

Ursa Major, Ursa Minor, and Polaris

bright and apparently isolated star. This is Polaris, the north pole star. It is a precise indicator of true north and always remains in the same position in the sky for an observer in a particular place. If you were viewing it from the north pole, it would be directly above your head, at the highest point in the sky. At latitude 45° north (the latitude of Minneapolis or Turin, for example), it appears exactly 45° above the northern horizon. At the equator, it rests on the line of the horizon. Polaris does not move in the course of the night, because it lies so close to the axis on which the Earth rotates. All the other stars appear to revolve around it: after an interval of an hour or two, it is easy to see how Ursa Major has changed orientation, as it has rotated around Polaris.

Polaris is the most brilliant star in the constellation Ursa Minor (the Little Dipper or Little Bear). This constellation extends between Ursa Major and

A map showing how an observer at latitude 45° north can locate the principal landmarks below the Big Dipper. Those shown are all observable when Ursa Major is passing south of Polaris, particularly at the beginning of spring at 22:00. In different seasons and at other times, only some of them are visible. ▽

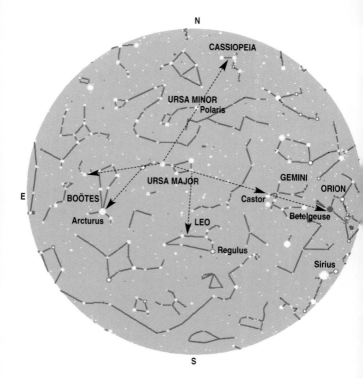

54

Polaris, and is made up of relatively faint stars. This makes it difficult to identify, especially if the sky is not completely dark.

FINDING THE OTHER PRINCIPAL LANDMARKS

Ursa Major and Ursa Minor act as signposts, enabling the observer to locate other landmarks in the night sky which may not be visible at all times. It is Ursa Major that supplies the most important directions. The constellation Leo, for example, is some distance away from and below it, so if the Big Dipper is close to the horizon, Leo will be below the horizon and unobservable. On the other hand, the constellation Cygnus is located above the Big Dipper and beyond Polaris. The two maps below demonstrate how to find the other major landmarks (stars and constellations) described in this chapter.

A map showing how an observer at latitude 45° north can locate the principal landmarks above the Big Dipper. All of these are visible when Ursa Major brushes the northern horizon, for example at the beginning of October around 22:00. ▽

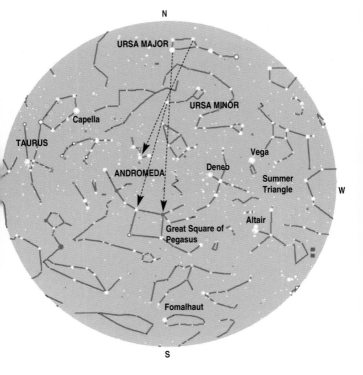

CASSIOPEIA

FINDING CASSIOPEIA

Just like Ursa Major, the constellation Cassiopeia never sets below the horizon for observers at latitudes above 40° north. It is another permanent landmark, visible in the sky at every hour of any night throughout the year. Its W-shaped pattern composed of five bright stars makes it readily identifiable. To find Cassiopeia, extend the line linking Dubhe and Merak in the Big Dipper (Ursa Major) to Polaris by approximately the same distance again. This brings you to β (Beta) Cassiopeiae (Caph), which marks the right-hand end of the W when this is viewed the right way up.

DIRECTIONS SUPPLIED BY CASSIOPEIA

Cassiopeia does not supply very many pointers enabling observers to find other stars or constellations, but it is an easy landmark to pick out, so it can be a great help in establishing the general orientation of the night sky. For instance, Andromeda, Pegasus, Pisces, Triangulum, and Aries are all located approximately below it when the W is viewed upright. To be precise, extending the line that joins γ (Gamma) and α (Alpha)

▽ *The constellation Cassiopeia as it appears in the night sky.*

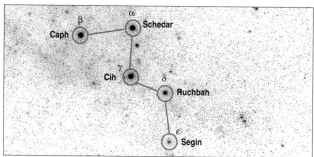

56

Cassiopeiae leads the observer directly to α (Alpha) Andromedae, Alpheratz, the brightest star in the Great Square of Pegasus. To the right of the W (again viewed upright) is the Summer Triangle, which connects Cygnus, Lyra, and Aquila. Just to the left of the W is the edge of the constellation Perseus. Its double open cluster, visible to the naked eye, is found on an extension of the line between γ (Gamma) and δ (Delta) Cassiopeiae. Finally, Cepheus, Ursa Minor, and Draco are all just above Cassiopeia.

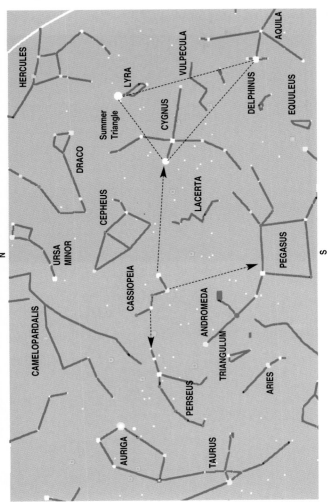

LEO

FINDING LEO

Leo is a large and beautiful constellation, but it is not visible all year round. As it lies near the celestial equator, it can only be seen in spring and toward the end of winter. It is located exactly below the Big Dipper of Ursa Major, so there is no point in trying to find it if the Big Dipper is only just above the northern horizon. By then it will be below the horizon (indicating, incidentally, that summer is nearly over).

▽ *The constellation Leo as it appears in the night sky.*

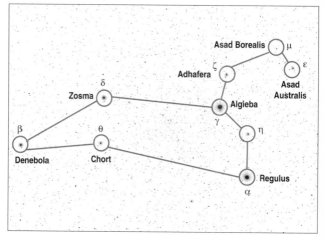

DIRECTIONS SUPPLIED BY LEO

Leo is extremely useful as a guide to finding some nearby constellations which have no particularly bright stars themselves, such as Hydra, Sextans, Cancer, Crater, Corvus, Coma Berenices, and Antlia. The relatively bright, solitary star slightly more than 20° below Regulus is Alphard, the principal star of Hydra.

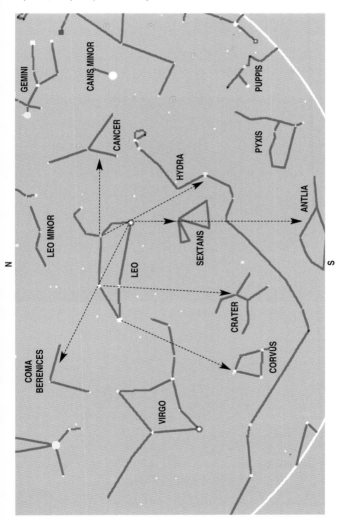

TAURUS AND THE PLEIADES

FINDING TAURUS

Taurus is a large winter constellation, appearing in the evening sky during November and December. At this time of year it rises above the southern horizon around 21:00. It is identifiable by its principal star Aldebaran, the fourteenth brightest star in the sky, which has a beautiful orange light. Just below Aldebaran is the so-called face of Taurus, a triangular shape formed by several stars belonging to the Hyades open cluster. Located 13° to the west of Aldebaran is a group of stars resembling a small pale cloud: this is the Pleiades open cluster, also known as the Seven Sisters.

Taurus, as it appears in the night sky, together with the Pleiades (which form part of the constellation). The photograph also shows a bright "star" that is not on the charts: this is the planet Mars. ▽

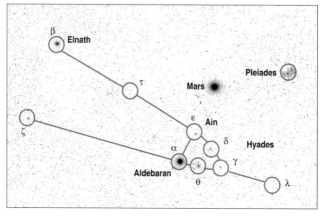

DIRECTIONS SUPPLIED BY TAURUS
AND THE PLEIADES

With the help of these two celestial landmarks, the constellations Cetus, Aries, Auriga, Triangulum, and Eridanus can easily be located. Following the line joining α (Alpha) and ζ (Zeta) Tauri brings the observer right into the center of the constellation Gemini.

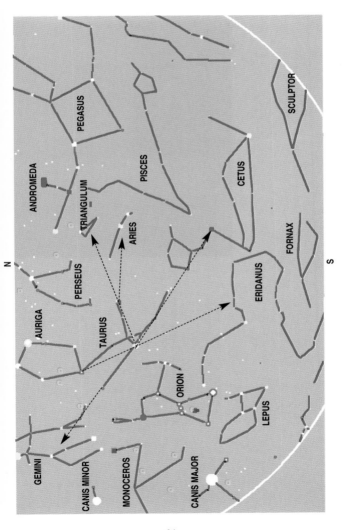

ORION

FINDING ORION

Orion is a fine, bright constellation and easy to identify in the winter sky, even from the center of a city. In January at around 21:00 it appears directly south. Its four bright "corner" stars, among them Betelgeuse and Rigel, surround three others arranged in a line that forms Orion's Belt. A little way below the easternmost star of Orion's Belt, the Orion Nebula (M42) appears as a milky blob.

The constellation Orion, in a long-exposure photograph. It can be seen like this with the unaided eye. ▷

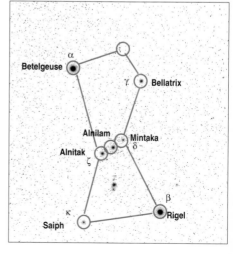

DIRECTIONS SUPPLIED
BY ORION

Orion is a key landmark for locating many other constellations that are not themselves easy to find. These include Lepus, Columba, Eridanus, Cetus, Monoceros, and also Canis Major, whose principal star is Sirius.

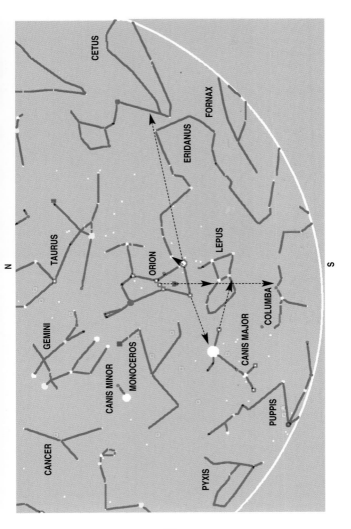

SIRIUS

FINDING SIRIUS

Sirius is not a constellation but a star, the brightest in the night sky. It is 8.61 light years from Earth and belongs to the constellation Canis Major. This constellation is not easily recognizable from its outline, but the brilliance of its principal star acts as a beacon that lights the way to other constellations. Like Orion, Sirius belongs to the winter sky, although it rises a little later (approximately two hours after Rigel).

The brilliant star Sirius appears as a large white disk in this long-exposure photograph. ▷

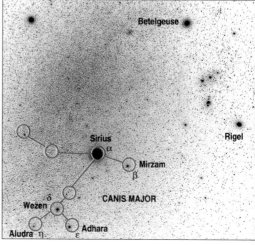

DIRECTIONS SUPPLIED BY SIRIUS

Sirius is the starting point for finding the constellations Puppis, Columba, Pyxis, Lepus, Hydra, and Monoceros.
To observers in high latitudes, however, Sirius appears very low on the horizon, and some of these constellations, such as Columba and Puppis, will not be visible.

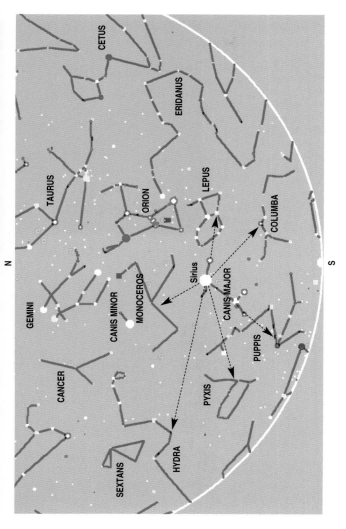

THE SUMMER TRIANGLE

FINDING THE SUMMER TRIANGLE

This is not a constellation, but a large pattern made by three bright stars belonging to three different constellations: Altair (in Aquila), Deneb (in Cygnus), and Vega (in Lyra). Together they form a huge, bright triangle high in the night sky, which is clearly visible in the months of July and August. Deneb and the triangle to which it belongs can be located by following the line linking Phekda and Megrez in Ursa Major. Another way to locate the Summer Triangle is to look directly overhead and find a bright star, bluish-white in color, situated close to the vertical. This is Vega, which can be recognized by its accompanying small parallelogram of four stars (magnitudes 3 and 4).

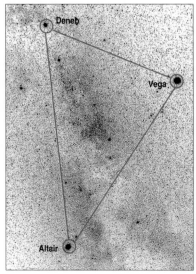

△ ▷ *The Summer Triangle as it appears to the naked eye. The huge "cluster" of stars at its center is part of the Milky Way.*

DIRECTIONS SUPPLIED BY THE SUMMER TRIANGLE

Its great size makes the Summer Triangle an excellent way of locating several nearby secondary constellations, such as Delphinus, Sagitta, Vulpecula, Equuleus, Scutum, Serpens Cauda, and Lacerta. Others further away can also be found using the Summer Triangle: these include Sagittarius, Ophiuchus, Aquarius, Capricornus, Pegasus, and Hercules.

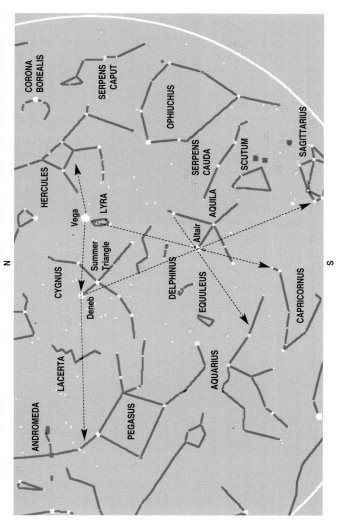

BOÖTES

FINDING BOÖTES

Boötes is a northern constellation, observable near the zenith in the evenings during the month of June. It can be found by extending the handle of the Big Dipper in Ursa Major. It passes extremely high overhead, and is partially circumpolar in latitudes above 65° north. Boötes has one very bright star, which is a useful navigational aid: this is Arcturus, with a magnitude of −0.1.

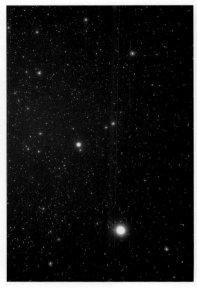

The constellation Boötes as it appears to the naked eye. ▷

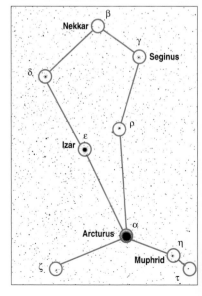

DIRECTIONS SUPPLIED BY BOÖTES

Right next to Boötes is the small constellation Corona Borealis, whose principal star is Alphecca. Continuing an alignment from Arcturus to Alphecca leads directly to the so-called Keystone at the center of the constellation Hercules. Boötes is also a landmark for locating Serpens, Ophiuchus, Virgo, Coma Berenices, and Canes Venatici.

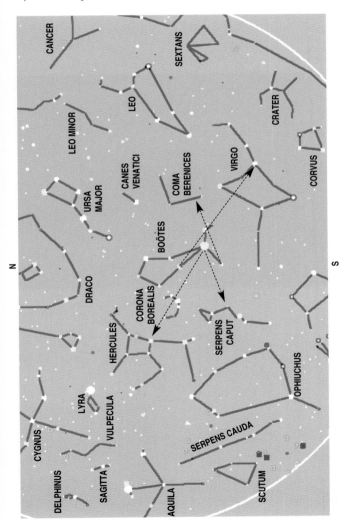

GREAT SQUARE OF PEGASUS

FINDING THE GREAT SQUARE OF PEGASUS

Pegasus is a relatively easy constellation to find, by extending the line between γ (Gamma) and α (Alpha) Cassiopeiae. Four stars of magnitude 2 to 2.9 form a large rectangle known as the Great Square of Pegasus. The brightest of these, Alpheratz, in fact belongs to the neighboring constellation Andromeda. The Great Square is not the entire constellation, but it is a very useful landmark in the fall sky.

The Great Square of Pegasus as it appears to the naked eye. ▽

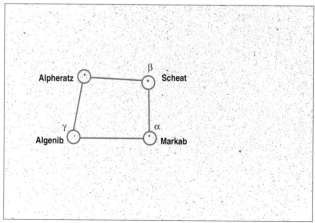

DIRECTIONS SUPPLIED BY
THE GREAT SQUARE OF PEGASUS

Locating the constellation Andromeda is no problem, thanks to the Great Square of Pegasus. It is also of great use in finding other constellations, including Triangulum, Pisces, Aries, Cetus, Aquarius, Capricornus, Equuleus, Delphinus, and Piscis Austrinus.

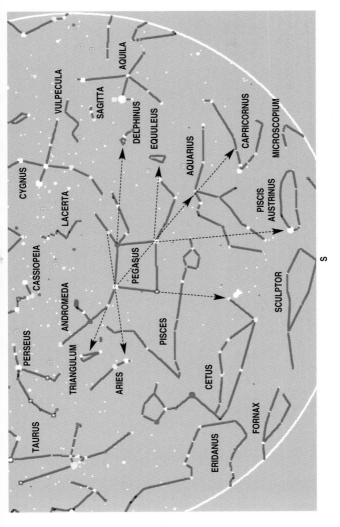

THE SOLAR SYSTEM

OVERVIEW

PLANETS AROUND A STAR

Our Solar System consists of a number of bodies all revolving around a star known as the Sun. There are eight planets and one dwarf planet trapped in its orbit: in order of distance from the Sun they are Mercury, Venus, Earth, Mars, Jupiter, Saturn, Uranus, Neptune, and Pluto. They all move in virtually the same plane, forming what could be described as an invisible disk. Just as the Sun has its planets, so most of the planets have satellites of their own, the exceptions being Mercury and Venus. The Earth's satellite, the Moon, is unusually large, with a diameter one-fourth of the Earth's. Mars has two small, rocky satellites, Phobos and Deimos, each a few kilometers in diameter. At the other end of the scale, Jupiter, Saturn, Uranus, and Neptune all have many satellites of various sizes.

But the Solar System does not consist solely of the major planets and their moons. There are many other, smaller bodies orbiting the Sun, including the asteroids, rocky objects more or less spherical in shape. Most of these are found in a belt between Mars and Jupiter. The largest, Ceres, is less than 1,000 kilometers in diameter, while the smallest ones are only a few meters across. Comets also belong to the Solar System. They differ from asteroids in being largely composed of ice, which evaporates into gas as it heats up. Comets travel around the Sun in very elongated orbits which take them a great distance away (beyond the dwarf planet Pluto), but also bring them into the inner Solar System, some approaching even closer to their parent star than Mercury. Some of them originate in a ring-shaped area, just beyond Neptune and Pluto, known as the Kuiper Belt. Others come from the more distant Oort Cloud, a vast spherical region surrounding the Solar System, thousands of millions of kilometers away (see p.131).

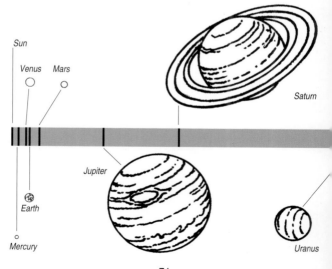

Sun

Venus Mars

Saturn

Jupiter

Earth

Mercury

Uranus

◁ *The Earth is the largest of the rocky planets.*

Mercury, Venus, Mars, Earth, and many satellites (including our own Moon) are solid bodies made of rock, upon which it is possible to walk. Jupiter, Saturn, Uranus, and Neptune, on the other hand, are large gaseous spheres without a solid surface. A spacecraft would be quite unable to land on them; it would just sink down into a mass of cloud. Pluto and a few satellites are solid spherical bodies like the Earth, but largely composed of (or covered in) ice. Asteroids and comets are much smaller, irregular bodies.

THE LAWS AND DIMENSIONS OF THE SOLAR SYSTEM

The Sun is absolute ruler of the Solar System. This star, 1,400,000 kilometers in diameter, contains 99.8% of the Solar System's total mass. The eight planets plus Pluto together make up only another 0.14%, while the remainder, approximately 0.06%, consists of asteroids and comets. Jupiter, which is by far the largest planet, has a mass 318 times that of the Earth; yet this still represents only one thousandth of the mass of the Sun. Jupiter is 5.2 AU and Pluto 39.8 AU from the Sun. The measurement of the distances separating the planets from the Sun revealed a relationship known as the Titius–Bode "law," named after the two German astronomers who formulated it in the eighteenth century. They divided the

The colored band represents the relative distances of the eight planets plus the dwarf planet Pluto from the Sun. The planets are drawn in scale with each other, but of course much exaggerated in size compared to the scale of distance. ▽

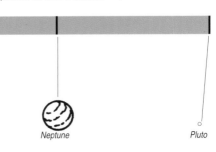

Neptune

Pluto

distance between the Sun and the outermost known planet (Saturn) into 100 sections or "parts," making Mercury 4 parts away, Venus 7 parts (or 4 + 3), Earth 10 (or 4 + 6), Mars 16 (or 4 + 12), and so on. In this series, the second figure of each pair is double that of the last. The theory predicted that a planet would be found at each of these distances from the sun, and it was remarkably accurate as far out as Saturn, except that no planet had been found at a distance of 28 (4 + 24) parts, or 2.8 AU. Astronomers searched for the missing object, and in 1801 Giuseppe Piazzi discovered Ceres at 2.77 AU, which seemed to confirm the law. Subsequently Uranus was discovered at a distance of 19.2 AU – close enough to the predicted figure of 196 to reinforce the theory. But Neptune and Pluto, both later discoveries, completely failed to conform to the pattern and relegated the Titius–Bode law to the status of a historical curiosity. Nevertheless, with this simple calculation astronomers can still work out the approximate distance from the Sun of most of the planets.

THE MECHANICS OF THE SOLAR SYSTEM

The three laws published by Johannes Kepler between 1609 and 1618, on the other hand, still form the foundation of our present-day understanding of planetary motion. Building on observations made before him by the Danish astronomer Tycho Brahe, Kepler succeeded in working out the paths taken by the planets through space.

Kepler's first law states that the orbit of a planet around the Sun is an ellipse, with the Sun at one focus. The second law (the Law of Equal Areas) states that the line joining a planet to the Sun sweeps out equal areas in equal intervals of time. That is to say that, when a planet passes its perihelion (the point of its orbit nearest the Sun), it is traveling faster than when it passes its aphelion (the point furthest from the Sun). Finally, Kepler's third law establishes a relationship between the time a planet takes to orbit the Sun and its distance from it. This law states that the squares of the periods of all the planets, expressed in years, are equal to

THE SOLAR SYSTEM IN FIGURES

Planet	Diameter	Orbital Period	Distance (AU)	Maximum Magnitude
Mercury	4,880 km	88 days	0.39	−1.2
Venus	12,104 km	224.7 days	0.72	−4.7
Earth	12,756 km	356.25 days	1	
Mars	6,792 km	1 yr 321 days	1.52	−2.8
Jupiter	142,800 km	11 yrs 314 days	5.20	−2.9
Saturn	120,000 km	29 yrs 167 days	9.54	−0.3
Uranus	51,118 km	84 yrs 7 days	19.22	5.5
Neptune	49,528 km	164 yrs 288 days	30.06	7.8
Pluto	2,320 km	248 yrs 197 days	39.54	13.7

the cubes of their semimajor axes (their average distance from the Sun), expressed in astronomical units. In the case of Jupiter, which orbits the Sun once every 11.86 years, this gives 11.86 squared, or 140.6, which equals the cube of 5.2, the number of astronomical units separating Jupiter from the Sun. Thus the law demonstrates that the greater a planet's distance from the Sun, the longer it takes to complete its orbit.

△ Jupiter, the largest planet in the Solar System, is a gaseous sphere.

HISTORY AND DISCOVERIES

Ever since Antiquity, astronomers have been aware that some stars moved among the others, which remained motionless. The ancient Greeks gave them the name of planets, which meant "wandering stars," but predicting their courses long remained an uncertain business. In the second century A.D., Ptolemy gave the first detailed description of the movement of the planets in his *Almagest*. He believed the Earth to be the center of the Universe, around which the other heavenly bodies (the planets, the Sun, and the Moon) revolved, each in its own orbit. Ptolemy resolved the problem of the retrograde motions of certain planets (such as Mars, see p.106) by interpreting them as epicycles, secondary orbits made in addition to a planet's normal motion. Ptolemy's system held sway until Copernicus's calculations, published in 1543, followed by Galileo's observations in 1610 with his new telescope, began to establish the idea of a Solar System with the Sun at its center and the Earth as merely one of its planets. Kepler subsequently discovered that the planets' orbits are elliptical, not circular. During the same period, improvements in optical instruments made it possible to see the known planets as they really were, and led to the discovery of new ones: Uranus, Neptune, and Pluto. In our own time, unmanned spacecraft have been able to take a close look at each of them – except Pluto.

OBSERVING THE SOLAR SYSTEM

It is only rarely that all the planets are on view together, although several can generally be seen in the sky at once. They almost seem to be arranged in a line, because they all move within a band a few degrees wide that straddles the Sun's apparent orbit, the ecliptic, thereby helping the observer to locate it.

THE EVOLUTION OF THE SOLAR SYSTEM

With all the knowledge that humankind has achieved today, we still cannot be sure how the Sun and its attendant planets were formed, several thousand million years ago. In attempting to sort out what actually happened, astronomers have been forced to juggle with all kinds of data accumulated in many different ways. Since the exploration of space began, followed by the Moon landing and close observation of many of the planets, much valuable information has been gathered. The planets' surfaces bear the traces of past events, enabling us to reconstruct the principal episodes in their history. In recent years, mainly thanks to the Hubble Space Telescope, we have been able to add to the picture by observing nebulae thousands of light years distant. They have given us, above all, an insight into the conditions that might have led to the formation of the Sun. Because of such advances, astronomers can now sketch in outline the origin and evolution of the Solar System.

THE BIRTH OF THE SUN

In the beginning, it would seem, there was a molecular cloud many light years across. The Milky Way still contains such clouds: they are what we call nebulae, and many of them can be observed by amateur astronomers. Under the effect of its own gravity, this immense cloud, composed of hydrogen and dust formed by the combustion of long-dead stars, began to collapse in upon itself, until its ever increasing density reached the point (at several thousand molecules per cubic centimeter) where contraction was halted by the action of magnetic forces within the matter itself.

In theory, the compression should have stopped there. But some external force, resulting perhaps from the explosion of a nearby supernova, emitted a shock wave capable of further compressing the cloud. The uneven distribution of the gas and dust within it caused clumps of denser matter to form. As these clumps contracted still further, the gases at their center came under ever higher pressure, and consequently they began to heat up.

In 1983, the US satellite IRAS detected infrared sources at the heart of such dense clumps measuring 0.3 to 1.6 light years in diameter, revealing

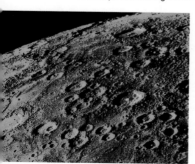

that stars were in the process of formation. It would seem that gravitational collapse leads to the creation of a spherical object at the center of the dense clump that is no longer gaseous but not yet a star. This infant stellar object, the

◁ *The dead surface of Mercury, pitted by the intense meteorite bombardment to which the planets were subjected until about 3,800 million years ago.*

△ *The Eagle Nebula (M16) photographed by the Hubble Space Telescope. The light spots visible at the top of the large cloud are evaporating gaseous globules (EGGs), at the heart of which new stars are forming. The Sun was formed in exactly the same way more than 4,500 million years ago.*

kernel of a future star, begins to draw the remainder of the material around it to create an outer layer. Stars of widely varying sizes can be formed in the same way, their mass depending on the amount of matter initially available. This seems to be the sequence of events that brought the Sun into being.

Still surrounded by thick clouds of gas and dust, the legacy of its primordial nebulous state, the nascent star grew ever hotter under the force of its own gravity, until massive thermonuclear reactions were triggered and a new star began to shine. In all, it had taken less than a million years for the original cloud of gas to give birth to the Sun. But some of the gas and dust, instead of falling into the Sun and adding to its mass, missed its target, as it were, and began to form a disk orbiting the new star. Similar structures have been observed round other stars, such as Beta Pictoris, the second brightest star in the constellation Pictor, which is not visible from mid-northern latitudes.

The Evolution of the Solar System

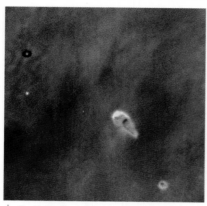

△ The Hubble Space Telescope revealed very young stars in the Great Nebula (M42), still enveloped by gaseous disks, which is perhaps how our own Solar System looked 4,500 million years ago.

GAS AND DUST

A little more than 4,500 million years ago, then, the Sun was still surrounded by a vast ring of orbiting dust and gas. Gradually the particles coalesced into larger grains of dust and, in their endless journey around the Sun, collisions between these created lumps of ever increasing size, growing from a few meters to several kilometers in diameter. To reach this point took some tens of millions of years, which is actually a fairly short period on the timescale of the evolution of the Solar System.

At the orbital distances of Mercury, Venus, Earth, and Mars, the dust and debris gradually consolidated into lumps of rock. At the distance of Jupiter, however, where it was much colder, the rocky objects became sheathed in ice, i.e. solidified gas. This difference led to the creation of terrestrial (rocky) planets and asteroids on the one hand, and gaseous planets and comets on the other (see pp.108–111 for asteroids, and pp.130–133 for comets).

Some of the larger rocky objects attracted the smaller ones to themselves and became what are known as protoplanets, the ancestors of the present planets. Now of far greater mass, they captured lesser bodies that passed within their gravitational field, in this way growing further until they became the familiar planets. Some of them pulled lesser planets into their orbits, and these became their satellites, while asteroids of all sizes continued to rain down upon their surfaces. This period of meteorite bombardment reached its peak some 4,500 million years ago, and maintained its intensity for about 700 million years. Over the last 3,800 million years, the Solar System has changed very little. The planets have mopped up, as it were, the gas and the dust from the surrounding space, and many of the asteroids too: collisions are rare events now. The craters on the Moon remain as a visible reminder of the meteorites which once pounded the planets, but in all the centuries that astronomers have been watching the sky through telescopes, they have witnessed only one collision of any significance, when fragments of Comet Shoemaker–Levy 9 crashed onto Jupiter in 1994.

This is not to say that similar events cannot happen on Earth. On June 30, 1908, in the Tunguska region of Siberia, a meteorite 30 meters in diameter disintegrated at a height of 10 kilometers, devastating an area of 2,000 square kilometers. Fortunately, the region was very sparsely populated. And 65 million years ago (quite recently, astronomically speaking) a huge meteorite smashed into the Earth in the Yucatán region of Mexico. Vast quantities of dust and debris, propelled into the atmosphere by the impact, caused a climatic shift that may have been responsible for the extinction of the dinosaurs. At the present time, however, the Solar System is enjoying a relatively calm phase, which should continue for the next 5,000 million years. After that, the Sun will come to the end of its life, which will occasion cataclysmic upheavals (see p.86).

ARE THERE OTHER SOLAR SYSTEMS?

Since our Sun has planets revolving around it, might there not be planets orbiting other stars? This question has prompted a good deal of research, which for a long time remained fruitless. In 1992, a team of radio astronomers detected three small planets in orbit round a pulsar, but so close to a neutron star (see pp.244–245), their environment would most probably be too hostile to support life. Late in 1995, two Swiss astronomers, Michel Mayor and Didier Queloz, discovered a planet almost the size of Jupiter orbiting the star 51 Pegasi (see p.184). Since then, other extra-solar planets, as they are called, have been found by other teams of astronomers.

Our own Solar System is by no means unique, then, but some statistical studies suggest that only 3% of stars of the solar type have planets orbiting them.

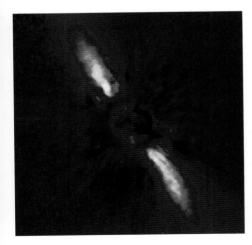

◁ The star Beta Pictoris is only a few hundred million years old and still retains a ring of dust. This has been shown to contain comets, indicating that objects several kilometers in diameter have already formed there. There are quite probably planets as well.

THE SUN

DATA

Average Distance from Center of Milky Way:
26,000 light years
Time taken to orbit Milky Way:
200 million years
Period of Rotation: 28 days
Diameter: 1.4 million kilometers
Mass: 1,000 times that of Jupiter
Surface Temperature: 5,500°C
Principal Planets: 9

AN ORDINARY STAR

The Sun is nothing more than an ordinary star, a ball of gas so hot that it produces light. It appears much brighter than the other stars only because of its proximity to Earth. Our second nearest star, Alpha Centauri, is at a distance of 4.3 light years, whereas the Sun is only 8 light minutes away. Both stars are more or less the same size: if one could view the Sun from the same distance as Alpha Centauri, it would appear much the same.

This star of our daytime has been illuminating the space around it for over 4,500 million years (see p.78). Its huge mass compresses the hydrogen of which it is chiefly composed, heating it and transforming it into helium by nuclear fusion. The gravitational compression is constantly counteracted by the expansion caused by the heat it produces, which makes the Sun in effect a thermonuclear fusion reactor contained by gravity. Every second, 4 million tonnes of hydrogen are fused into helium, releasing radiation. The temperature at the center of this giant thermal reactor is 15 million degrees Celsius, while the surface temperature is no higher than 5,500°C.

The Sun's surface (the photosphere) is composed of convective cells or "granules," each about 1,000 kilometers in diameter, which can be seen with large telescopes. Convection currents within them carry the internal heat to the surface. The dark

◁ The Sun as it appears in a telescope: a glowing ball with darker patches scattered across its surface.

spots scattered across the Sun's surface are relatively cool regions (about 4,000°C), concentrated along the lines of its magnetic field. Above the photosphere is the chromosphere, a layer whose temperature is over one million degrees Celsius at its top.

Ejections of matter from the photosphere can sometimes be seen in the chromosphere, and are known as prominences. These huge plumes, millions of kilometers in length, persist for only a few minutes; seen through a telescope, they are one of the most amazing sights the sky has to offer.

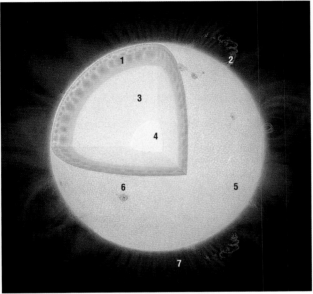

△ Structure of the Sun: 1. Convective zone; 2. Prominence; 3. Radiative zone; 4. Core (15,000,000°C); 5. Photosphere (5,500°C); 6. Sunspot; 7. Chromosphere.

HISTORY AND DISCOVERIES

The nature of the Sun long remained a mystery to astronomers. But, thanks to the work of the Polish astronomer Nicolas Copernicus, around 1600 it began to be understood that only the immense distance of the stars in the sky prevented them from shining just as brightly as the Sun. After that it was a short step to understanding that the Sun was itself a star, albeit a very close one.

In the 1860s, having calculated the mass of the Sun and theorizing that it was composed of carbon (the most efficient fuel known at the time), astronomers worked out that it could only have enough reserves to burn for 5,000 years from the time it began. But at the same time, geologists and biologists were demonstrating that minerals and certain living species had existed on Earth for millions of years or more. Lord Kelvin and Hermann von Helmholtz put forward the theory that the Sun was gradually contracting, which would enable it to shine for between 30 and 100 million years; meanwhile, geologists revised their estimate of the age of the oldest minerals upwards to some 1,000 million years. It was not until 1905, when Albert Einstein published his theory of relativity (in particular, the equation $E = mc^2$), that it became possible to calculate how long the nuclear reactions at the Sun's core could continue, and the answer was approximately 10,000 million years.

OBSERVING THE SUN

In addition to being the easiest star to observe, the Sun is also the most dangerous. Strict precautions are essential, because looking at the Sun, either with or without the aid of a telescope, can cause serious lesions to the retina, resulting in permanent sight loss. Never look directly at the Sun with the naked eye during an eclipse, for example. Special protection is vital if accidents are to be avoided.

It is possible to observe the Sun with the naked eye and without risk of injury by looking through a sheet of Mylar (a silvery synthetic material used in survival blankets, etc.). Sunglasses do not give adequate protection. A solar filter screwed onto the back of a monocular may also be used. This form of protection, though not very reliable when used with a telescope, is quite sufficient for viewing with the naked eye. The only drawback is

Prominences are spectacular ejections of matter from the Sun which change from one minute to the next. Special filters or a coronagraph (an instrument that creates an artificial solar eclipse) are necessary for observing them. ▷

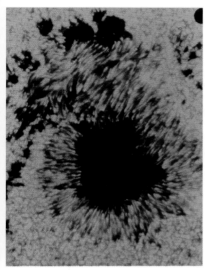

△ *Close-up of sunspots and surrounding granulation, taken at the Pic du Midi de Bigorre observatory in France.*

that, unless you have two filters, you can only use one eye. In poor conditions, the unaided observer will only see a small disk of uniform brightness, but under good conditions, during periods of intense solar activity, the dark sunspots may be large enough to be detected. Even a small astronomical telescope is sufficient to examine details like these on the Sun's surface. With ×50 magnification, as long as there is any solar activity, sunspots will be visible as black blotches, gray at the edges. It is possible to watch them change shape and even disap-

pear, to be replaced by new ones over as short a period as one day. They also seem to move longitudinally, although this is actually due to the Sun itself rotating. If a sunspot lasts long enough, it is possible to track it and see it return to its original position after 28 days, which is the time taken by the Sun to rotate once upon its axis. All these observations can be successfully accomplished with a beginner's instrument 2 to 4 inches (50 to 100 mm) in diameter, provided it is equipped with adequate protection against the Sun's light. Some telescopes of this standard are sold with a solar filter that screws onto the eyepiece, but the problem here is that it is usually far too close to the focal plane, where the Sun's rays converge. As a result, it is subjected to heat intense enough to break it, making it extremely risky as a protective device. The filter on a 2½-inch (60 mm) refractor is much less likely to break, but once a refractor's diameter reaches 4 inches (100 mm) the risk again becomes a real one. It can be significantly reduced by pointing the instrument at the Sun for no more than 30 seconds at a time, and then allowing the filter to cool down for one minute. In addition, stopping down the lens aperture to 2 inches (50 mm) will lessen the likelihood of overheating the filter. Another technique, this time without a filter, is to view the Sun's image projected onto a white screen placed several centimeters behind the eyepiece. But when using this method you must remember that the instrument is unprotected, and that nobody must be allowed to look through the eyepiece under any circumstances.

The Sun

The best method of all is to mount a protective device in front of the objective, and suitable glass filters can be bought for instruments of all sizes. The only drawback is their cost: good quality filters tend to be expensive. But they allow the Sun to be studied for long periods in complete safety, without loss of resolution. Less costly is fixing a sheet of Mylar in front of the lens, although this will not last very long. After being used a few times, the material will develop creases which can let light rays through, so at the slightest sign of damage it should be replaced immediately. No adequate protection is available for a telescope's finder, so avoid using this to locate the Sun. It is better to aim the tube at the Sun by looking at the shadow it throws on the ground. When the shadow is at its smallest, the Sun should be in view. Fine

adjustment may be necessary. If your instrument has an aperture of 8 inches (200 mm) or more, you should acquire a filter that fits over the objective. This is because the concentrated heat of the Sun shining through the lens makes it impossible to use a filter on the eyepiece, and the heat could also damage the instrument's optical surfaces. Detailed

THE DEATH OF THE SUN

The Sun still has enough hydrogen to continue shining for another 5,000 million years. Then, one day in the distant future when almost all its hydrogen has been transformed into helium, the thermonuclear reactions will cease and its energy output will drop. The helium will contract and, under the pressure of its own mass, fuse into the heavier elements carbon and oxygen. Meanwhile, the Sun's gaseous outer layer will have started on a long process of expansion lasting some hundreds of millions of years, until Mercury and Venus have been enveloped. By this time the Sun will be a large, red globe, visible 1,600 light years away. Its core will then reactivate and expel the gases layer by layer, creating a planetary nebula. At its center the Sun, now a white dwarf, will gradually cool down and finally die.

△ One way of observing the Sun safely is to project its image onto a white screen.

◁ When observing the Sun, with or without a telescope, adequate eye protection is essential.

study of sunspots is possible with an instrument of this size, and brighter patches called faculae also become visible. An H-alpha filter (which costs almost as much as the telescope itself) is ideal for studying prominences at the edge of the Sun's disk.

87

MERCURY

THE PLANET WITH A HEART OF IRON

Mercury was formed 4,500 million years ago by the gradual accretion of innumerable small bits of rock, although its development also appears to have been affected by some cataclysmic event. Mercury is by far the densest planet in the Solar System, with an iron core that accounts for 40% of its volume and two-thirds of its total mass. The origins of a body containing so much iron are inexplicable through the straightforward process of accretion, even though Mercury was formed in a region very close to the Sun where the lighter elements (such as hydrogen, helium, and oxygen) had been blown away by the solar wind, leaving behind only silicates. Astronomers think that an enormous meteorite may have struck Mercury while it was being formed, dislodging its rocky coating, which was dispersed in space. A predominantly ferrous planet remained.

Observation of the planet points up another problem: its surface has apparently remained unchanged for 3,900 million years, which is an unnaturally long time. Even after the period of intense meteorite bombardment had ended, further craters appeared on the surfaces

Mercury's surface is as black as coal and, like that of the Moon, is pitted by craters interspersed with smooth plains. ▷

of the Moon and the other planets, but this is not the case with Mercury. Neither is any trace of volcanic activity visible on its coal-black surface, which reflects only 5.5% of the light it receives from the Sun. Moreover, the Mariner 10 spacecraft detected a weak magnetic field there, which provided further evidence that the planet possesses a very large iron core. But its extremely slow period of rotation (59 days), and the absence of even extinct volcanic activity, would seem to suggest that the core is not liquid.

Mercury is about the same size as Callisto, one of the Galilean moons of Jupiter, and has virtually no atmosphere at all. Traces of helium have been discovered, however, which could have been ejected by the Sun and captured in the short term by Mercury.

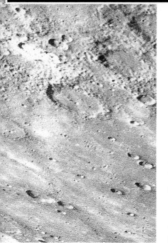

△ The Caloris Basin on Mercury is 1,300 km in diameter and was created by the impact of a gigantic meteorite.

HISTORY AND DISCOVERIES

The planet Mercury, just like Venus, Mars, Jupiter, and Saturn, was known to the ancients, and it has long been observed by telescope, though astronomers have had little success in making out any detail on its surface. The first problem posed by the planet concerns its orbit around the Sun. In 1859, the French astronomer Urbain Le Verrier (who a few years earlier had predicted where the planet Neptune would be found)

Mercury

published a paper in which he attributed the slow drift of Mercury's perihelion to the presence of another planet even closer to the Sun.

This hypothetical planet was named Vulcan, although it had never been seen. In the twentieth century, however, Mercury's motion was explained by Albert Einstein, using his theory of relativity.

At the end of the nineteenth century, the Italian astronomer Giovanni Schiaparelli made an approximate map of the planet, which was imitated in the 1920s by Eugène Antoniadi, but even then no information of any significance had been collected about Mercury. In 1965, observations made by the Arecibo radio telescope in Puerto Rico revealed that the planet rotates on its own axis in just under 59 days, precisely two-thirds of the time it takes to orbit the Sun.

Only one space probe, Mariner 10, has completed a mission to Mercury. It passed over the planet three times, on March 29 and September 21, 1974, and again on March 16, 1975. But each time the same hemisphere of the planet's surface was lit by the Sun, so even today astronomers only know what one half of it looks like.

The landscape revealed by the spacecraft bears a strong resemblance to that of the Moon, with a surface crust showing similar marks of meteorite scarring. In 1991, astronomers thought they might have detected ice at the bottom of some of the craters, for the light of the Sun never reaches the bottom of those near the planet's poles, and their temperature remains at a constant −170° C. Ice deposited there by comets could indeed have survived for thousands of millions of years, but this discovery still remains to be confirmed. The only means of doing this is to send another space probe, which may happen in 2012 when the European Space Agency hopes to send an unmanned craft, BepiColombo.

OBSERVING MERCURY

Mercury is not at all easy to see. The planet never moves further away than 28° from the Sun, which means that it sets and rises a maximum of 2 hours and 15 minutes after or before the Sun does. It follows that the planet only appears at times when the sky is not completely dark, and this explains why so few amateur astronomers have ever seen Mercury.

For the best chance of success, it is helpful to know when the maximum elongations (angles from the Sun) will occur. In mid-northern latitudes, the best opportunities will be found in the eastern elongations during spring, at the beginning of May, and in the western elongations during fall, at the end of October.

Finally, there are rare occasions when the planet may be observed without too much difficulty: namely, total eclipses of the Sun. Mercury, whose maximum magnitude is −0.7, can be located during an eclipse on a line joining the Sun to Venus, or any other visible planet. Once found, it is possible to keep the planet under observation in daylight, even after the eclipse is over.

Viewed with a telescope, Mercury may be seen to pass through its phases, just as Venus does. When the planet is at maximum illumination (and therefore at its greatest distance from us), its apparent angular diameter is at most 4.6″ (scarcely more than that of Uranus), while when it appears as a crescent, it reaches a maximum of 12.9″. Some indistinct dark patches can be observed on the planet's surface with a good telescope at least 6 inches (150 mm) in diameter, but what they are can still only be guessed at.

◁ The area at the antipodes of the Caloris Basin. The crazing of the surface was caused by a massive shock wave from the meteorite strike that formed the Basin on the far side of the planet. The Petrarch Crater subsequently filled with lava, giving it the smooth appearance of a lunar sea.

Venus

DATA

Second Planet from the Sun
Average Distance from the Sun: 0.72 AU
Sidereal Revolution Period: 224.7 days
Sidereal Rotation Period: 243.02 days (retrograde)
Oblateness: 0
Axial Inclination: 177.4°
Diameter: 12,104 km (95% of that of Earth)
Volume: 85% of that of Earth
Mass: 82% of that of Earth
Surface Temperature: 470°C
Atmospheric Pressure at Surface: 93 bars
Moons: 0

AN INHOSPITABLE PLANET

△ A radar image of Venus from the Magellan probe, revealing surface relief through the blanket of clouds.

Because of its size, its position in the Solar System, and its appearance from space, Venus has long been thought of as Earth's twin sister. But its atmosphere, topped with clouds containing sulfuric acid, and its surface temperature, capable of melting lead, make it a nightmare world very different from our own. In addition, its geology is unusual: the system of plate tectonics that operates on Earth is not present on Venus, where the surface features have all been created by volcanic activity. Like the other planets in the Solar System, Venus was formed 4,500 million years ago by the accretion of many smaller, rocky bodies. At that period, its overheated surface expelled the gases of which its atmosphere is now composed. But Venus is some 40 million kilometers closer to the Sun than Earth, and correspondingly hotter. This difference explains why the water vapor did not condense into oceans there, as it did on Earth. Instead, water vapor and carbon dioxide produced a strong greenhouse effect which warmed the atmosphere still further. Exposure to ultraviolet radiation from the Sun probably dispersed most of the water vapor into space, so that there is almost none left today. Some astronomers believe that the lack of water on the planet, which accounts for the exceptional hardness of Venusian rock, may also explain the absence of tectonic plates. On Earth, tectonic movement, in which some layers of rock plunge down towards the interior while others rise to the surface, allows 95% of

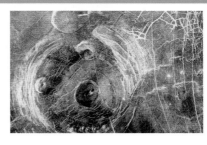

Venus's coronae are peculiar circular formations not seen anywhere else in the Solar System. ▷

the planet's internal energy to be released. The theory is that the inflexible surface crust of Venus cannot deform, and this prevents the tectonic movement that takes place on Earth. But results obtained by the US Magellan spacecraft appear to show that the planet's surface is only 500 million years old, a conclusion supported by the number of meteorite craters (about a thousand in all). Despite the protection given by Venus's atmosphere, the number would be much higher if the surface were 4,500 million years old. So, even without a system of tectonic plates, the planet's surface has somehow changed over the course of time. Since it seems unlikely that even the many volcanoes on Venus could have produced such changes, scientists have put forward various theories as to what may have happened. One is that the solid crust may have thickened to the point where it raised the planet's internal temperature, and once a certain point was reached the hot molten rock of the interior broke through the crust and flooded the surface, completely reshaping it. After the lava had cooled down and solidified, the cycle was repeated time after time.

Despite its proximity and many similarities to Earth, Venus has clearly had a very different past, and its unique features are still not fully understood. The coronae, circular formations up to 200 kilometers in diameter consisting of concentric ripples, are believed to be due to rising magma causing

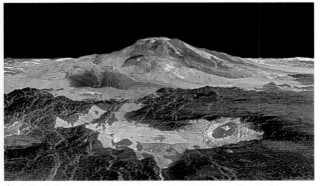

△ *Unlike Earth, the surface of Venus is not covered by shifting continental plates, although it has thousands of volcanoes of many different types.*

VENUS

the surface to bulge upward. When the magma subsides, the surface slumps back and fractures, leaving a circular corona. The planet's great domes, volcanoes around 25 kilometers in diameter but only 750 meters high, are thought to be this shape because the magmas that formed them were highly viscous.

HISTORY AND DISCOVERIES

Venus was first observed with the aid of a telescope by Galileo in 1610. Following its course over several months, he noticed that, like the Moon, Venus passed through different phases. This finding proved important because it reinforced Copernicus's theory of a heliocentric universe, advanced 66 years before. Galileo demonstrated that, with the aid of a basic telescope, it was possible to see when Venus was in its fullest phase, looking just like the full moon. He also noticed that during this phase its diameter appeared very small, but that when it was just a thin crescent, its diameter seemed much greater. This showed conclusively that Venus revolved around the Sun. In spite of all the technical improvements in astronomical instruments during the succeeding centuries, knowledge of Venus advanced very little. The advent of the space age made new discoveries possible, however, and in 1962 the US Mariner 2 probe became the first spacecraft to approach Venus, to within 36,600 kilometers. It found that the temperature at the planet's surface was around 450°C and that the surface was quite dry. On October 19, 1967, Mariner 5 measured the exact equatorial diameter of the planet and showed that most of its enveloping atmosphere, which is more than 100 kilometers thick, was composed of carbon dioxide gas. Just previously, the Russian Venera 4 module had been the first craft to land on the planet and take measurements from its surface. A total of 15 Russian probes were to land on Venus: in 1975, Venera 9 became the first to

Venus is permanently hidden beneath thick cloud, seen here by the Mariner 10 spacecraft. ▷

send back pictures of the surface. The two Vega craft, en route to observe Halley's Comet in 1984, released a landing craft and an atmospheric balloon. In 1974, the US probe Mariner 10 obtained the first images of the whole planet that showed the dense cloud formations enfolding it. Pioneer Venus produced the first radar map of the planet after its arrival in 1978, and higher-resolution radar data gathered by the Magellan mission between 1989 and 1994 enabled scientists to begin studying the planet's geology.

OBSERVING VENUS

Finding Venus is not difficult, since it is the brightest object in the sky after the Sun and the Moon. Look for it in the west just after sunset, or in the east just before sunrise. It looks like a large, white star which does not twinkle. But the Evening Star, as the planet is often called, is not always visible: when it passes behind the Sun (opposition) or directly between the Sun and the Earth (conjunction), it disappears from view. The best way to locate it is to consult an astronomical calendar. Viewed with 10×50 binoculars, Venus still looks like a bright point of light, except when it is passing closest to the Earth: then it can be recognized as a narrow crescent. It is only when seen in a small telescope with about $\times 35$ magnification that it takes on the appearance of a planet. Just before or after opposition, with an apparent angular diameter of only 10″, it looks like a tiny, brilliant white ball, but when as it approaches conjunction, the crescent may reach a diameter of 65″. Either way, the planet is quite dazzling. If you can start observing before sunrise, you should be able to keep it in view during daylight and, because the contrast between it and the sunlit sky is less strong, daytime observation is less strenuous on the eyes. However, it is impossible to see any detail on the planet's surface using amateur equipment. With a powerful telescope and an ultra-violet filter, it is just possible to glimpse the famous cloud formation, shaped like a sideways Y, first observed by exploring spacecraft.

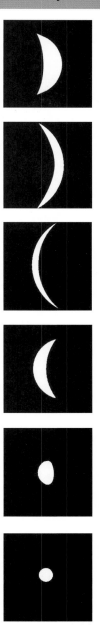

A telescopic view of the different phases of Venus. ▷

THE MOON

A DEAD PLANET

The surface of the Moon is an immense desert, pockmarked with craters of every size, extending over an area of 37,960,000 square kilometers. It has been petrified for hundreds of millions of years, and has been marked by all the meteorite bombardments in the history of the Solar System. The evolution of the Moon itself began a little over 4,500 million years ago. But though the process that formed the planets, both terrestrial and gaseous,

is more or less understood, what precisely led to the formation of the Moon remains a problem to scientists. If one assumes that it was formed in the same circumstances as the Earth, surely it should have a similar geological composition. But this is not the case, for the Moon contains significantly less iron. This fact led to a theory that it might have been formed in another region of the Solar System, where the predominant elements were different, and was subsequently drawn into the Earth's orbit. But this hypothesis appears untenable, since a planet can only capture a satellite that is already in a neighboring orbit, so it must have been formed in the same region as the Earth. Since 1975, astronomers have come to believe in the theory of a collision

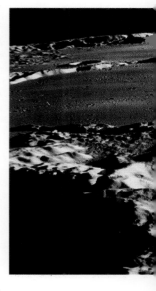

between the young Earth and a protoplanet the size of Mars. This would not have been a head-on collision, but a tangential one, in which the two astronomical bodies brushed against each other, as it were. The protoplanet would have been shattered, the rocky crust breaking into pieces and separating from the ferrous core. The iron core would have gone into orbit around the Earth before crashing onto it only a matter of hours later. In this short space of time, the debris from the crust would have begun to consolidate while in orbit, to form an object of significant size – the Moon – soon after. This account accords with the Moon's geological composition.

A COOLING PROCESS

The oldest rocks collected by astronauts on the Apollo missions are 4,550 million years old, and date from the period when the Moon was formed. Then, the Solar System was still packed with gases, dust, and rocky debris, which rained down ceaselessly upon the planets. These repeated impacts released intense heat, and the Moon became an incandescent sphere

The age-old lunar surface is bespattered with craters from meteor strikes. ▷

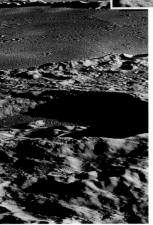

◁ *The lunar seas are large meteorite craters filled with lava that subsequently solidified.*

entirely covered with an ocean of magma to a depth of 450 kilometers. Over the next 100 million years, the lava cooled and began to crystallize. The densest materials present (olivine and pyroxene) sank towards the center of the planet, creating a mantle, while the lighter materials (feldspars) formed its surface crust. This crust is still visible today, in the light-colored areas known as the lunar highlands.

The Moon

Between 4,400 and 3,800 million years ago, an intense hail of meteorites pulverized the surface, leaving large scars that are still visible, such as the craters Clavius and Gassendi. At the same time, immense basins were created by the impact of larger bodies. About a hundred million years later, these began to be filled by flows of molten basalt, forming large, smooth plains: the lunar seas. The process continued for some 500 million years until, with the Moon's internal energy exhausted, volcanic activity ceased. A few later lava eruptions occurred, flowing over the already solidified surface, but the Moon today is a dead planet pitted by impact scars. Even the mountain ranges that fringe the seas (such as the Apennines) are just the edges of gigantic craters thrown up by meteorite collisions. The short duration of the Moon's volcanic activity (from 3,800 to 3,200 million years ago) probably accounts for the virtual absence of volcanoes like those on Earth. The seas cover 31.2% of the visible side of the Moon, but only 2.6% of its far side, where the crust is thicker. Soundings have shown that the surface crust, which averages 60 to 80 kilometers thick, hides a deep, slowly cooling mantle. At the center is an iron core about 300 kilometers across.

HISTORY AND DISCOVERIES

Until the invention of the telescope, the nature of the Moon remained a mystery. Some thought it to be a giant crystal, while others maintained it

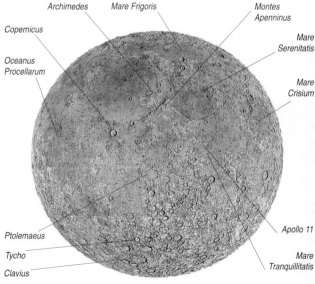

Archimedes   Mare Frigoris   Montes Apenninus

Copernicus

Oceanus Procellarum

Mare Serenitatis

Mare Crisium

Ptolemaeus

Tycho

Clavius

Apollo 11

Mare Tranquillitatis

△ General map of the Moon, for use with small telescopes, binoculars, or with the unaided eye.

△ *Twelve astronauts explored the Moon between 1969 and 1972.*

was an immense mirror reflecting the Earth's image. It was only in the sixteenth century that it came to be considered as a world in its own right, when Leonardo da Vinci concluded that the dark patches on its surface were continents and the lighter ones oceans. When Galileo made the first telescopic observation of the Moon in 1610, he confirmed the view that it was a planet made up of continents and oceans.

Mapping the Moon

Galileo drew everything he saw there, but was unable to explain the craters, which he described as "high, circular plains." Though the lithographs he made were only rough sketches, they were enough to send shock waves through the Church. The Moon, the Earth's own sister planet, became a destination to be explored and possessed by astronomers, just as the great navigators crossed the oceans of the Earth to claim and name new lands. Astronomers throughout the seventeenth century continued to map this new world in the sky, giving names to the dark patches they found there and which they believed to be seas, such as Mare Tranquillitatis, Mare Serenitatis, and Mare Frigoris. The craters in their turn were named after great men, like Aristotle, Archimedes, Tycho, and even Copernicus, whose theories about the Universe ignited one of the biggest controversies in the whole history of science. In the eighteenth century, advances in optics enabled the German astronomer Johann Schröter to produce the first really accurate map of the Moon. He also searched for traces of the Selenites, the supposed inhabitants of the Moon, who had captured the popular imagination at the time.

One Small Step for a Man ...

In the twentieth century, the Moon was finally explored by both manned and unmanned spacecraft. In December 1968, three men (Frank Borman, James Lovell, and William Anders) circumnavigated the Moon for the first time in Apollo 8, and on July 21, 1969, Neil Armstrong and Edwin Aldrin of the Apollo 11 mission became the first to set foot on its surface. By December 1972, a total of a dozen astronauts had walked on

The Moon

the Moon, and between them they brought back almost 400 kilograms of rock samples. Some of them even drove over the Moon's surface in a special all-terrain vehicle. While the Americans were enjoying these successes, the USSR landed several unmanned craft on the Moon. Two remote-controlled robots (Lunokhods) traveled dozens of kilometers across its surface, and the Luna 16, 20, and 24 probes collected and brought back small quantities of samples. In 1994, the US spacecraft Clementine went into orbit around the Moon, producing a map of the whole surface that included precise altitude data. This finally lifted the veil on a 270,000 km² region near the planet's south pole, about which little had been known.

OBSERVING THE MOON

The naked eye is all you need to start observing the Moon. With an apparent angular diameter of 0.5°, it is large enough for the dark areas that are its seas to be visible. Mare Crisium, Mare Tranquillitatis, Mare Serenitatis, Oceanus Procellarum, and Mare Imbrium are all identifiable without any instrument.

The Moon passes through phases in the course of a lunar month. Just after new moon, a narrow crescent appears in the sky soon after sunset. It is easy to make out the part of the Moon that is still dark, as it seems to give off a faint glow (known as "earthshine"). Seen from the Moon at this time, the Earth would be almost completely illuminated (full earth, as it were), and the large amount of solar light reflected from our planet illuminates the dark area faintly, making it visible from Earth. With a telescope, it is easy to spot the principal lunar craters lit by earthshine. When the right-hand half of the Moon is illuminated, this is its first quarter. One week after that, the Moon's face is completely bright: full moon. Another week later, only its left half is illuminated: this is its last quarter. It is new moon when the planet is invisible. Each phase recurs after 29.5 days, and this period is known as a synodic month, lunation, or phase cycle. The time taken by the Moon

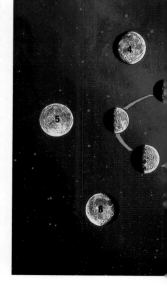

The main stages in the Moon's orbit around the Earth, showing its corresponding phases (anticlockwise): new moon (1), crescent (2), first quarter (3), waxing gibbous (4), full moon (5), waning gibbous (6), last quarter (7), crescent (8). ▷

◁ The crater Copernicus, 85 kilometers across, is one of the most spectacular on the Moon.

to make a complete orbit of the Earth is called a sidereal month.

With binoculars, the largest craters, such as Copernicus, Tycho (with its bright radiating lines), and Clavius, are quite easily seen. Other features are also identifiable, such as the mountain range known as the Montes Apenninus (the Apennines), and Sinus Iridum (the Bay of Rainbows). Even low magnification (×35) reveals craters that are only a few kilometers in diameter. An 8-inch (200 mm) telescope will show features less than one kilometer across. The general map on page 98 is a guide to the Moon's most prominent features, but a detailed atlas will enable you to get the most benefit from observing the Moon with a telescope. This is best done at times other than full moon, when the angle of the Sun's light throws the lunar features into sharp relief.

MARS

DATA

Fourth Planet from the Sun
Average Distance from the Sun: 1.52 AU
Sidereal Revolution Period: 1 year, 321 days
Sidereal Rotation Period: 24h 37m 23s
Oblateness: 0.006
Axial Inclination: 25.2°
Diameter: 6,795 km
Volume: 15% of that of Earth
Mass: 11% of that of Earth
Surface Temperature: −40°C (average)
Atmospheric Pressure at Surface: 0.08 bars
Satellites: 2

THE DESERT PLANET

Mars appears to be nothing but an endless expanse of dun-colored sand and rock, reminiscent of the Sahara or the Gobi desert. Immense seasonal sandstorms that can envelop the planet's entire surface are about all that disturbs this dead world. But its desolate landscape does offer some evidence that this small planet, half the size of Earth, was not always a static, featureless waste. Here and there are dried-up river beds, craters strewn with debris, enormous dead volcanoes, and gaping canyons, all pointing to the possibility that long ago the planet may have resembled our own – not the Earth as it is now, but as it was 4,000 million years ago.

The discoveries made by the exploratory US Viking missions have enabled astronomers to piece together the story of the planet's evolution since its formation. Between 4,500 and 3,800 million years ago, just like Earth and Venus, Mars was subjected to an intense bombardment of meteorites. During this period, the planet's internal energy gave rise to intense volcanic activity at its surface, spewing out the more volatile materials such as carbon dioxide and water vapor to form a dense, warm atmosphere, though not one that could support life as we know it. There could also have been water streaming across its surface in liquid form, as witness the dry river beds that date from this period. It is even possible that there were lakes and seas. The

◁ *Mars seen by the Hubble Space Telescope*

102

Red Planet, as it has long been called, resembles Earth in many ways, although it is colder, since Mars is further from the Sun. If there ever was life on Mars, it would have begun at that period, for at the same time and under similar conditions there were micro-organisms present on Earth.

But the life of Mars and of any possible Martians was cut short. This neighbor of ours was too small to maintain much internal energy, and it gradually ran down. Volcanic activity ceased, preventing the atmos-

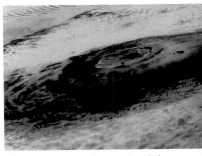

△ Olympus Mons, the largest volcano in the Solar System, last erupted 800 million years ago. This immense dome is 600 kilometers across and stands 27 kilometers high.

phere from renewing itself. Some of the carbon dioxide evaporated into space, and the rest reacted with elements on the surface to form carbonates. While carbon dioxide from the carbonates on Earth is constantly returned to the atmosphere by volcanoes, the Martian atmosphere became ever more rarefied until it all but vanished. Water could not remain liquid under such conditions: it either evaporated into space or froze beneath the surface. Any form of microbial life would have disappeared too.

Dried-up Watercourses

Water has since only appeared sporadically on this planet devoid of atmosphere, such as when a meteorite collided with the surface, or when occasional outbursts of volcanic activity took place. When Tharsis, the plateau where the most spectacular volcanoes in the whole of the Solar

System are to be found (including Olympus Mons, 27 kilometers high), returned briefly to life 800 million years ago, parts of the surface crust would have heated up again, melting quantities of ice that flowed briefly as powerful rivers.

The watercourses left by these huge rivers show no apparent source, and they lead nowhere. Without sufficient atmospheric pressure, the water could only have remained in a liquid state for a short period. It is thought that a good deal of water may still remain beneath the arid surface of Mars.

◁ The Valles Marineris, which starts at the foot of the volcanic plateau of Tharsis, is the most spectacular canyon in the Solar System. It is 5,000 kilometers in length, 600 kilometers wide, and in places 7 kilometers deep.

Mars

To observers, Mars is a planet of contrasts, with the smooth plains of its northern hemisphere on the one hand, and the uplands and craters of the south on the other. Here Olympus Mons, the largest volcano known, stands next to Valles Marineris, the longest and deepest canyon in the Solar System, where rivers once mightier than the Amazon have left their mark in a region now drier than the Sahara.

△ *The dried-up bed of the Mangala, a river that probably flowed 3,800 million years ago, winding through the southern uplands and down into the great plains of the north.*

HISTORY AND DISCOVERIES

In 1610, Galileo became the first man to observe Mars with a telescope, but with his primitive instrument he could only see it as a reddish disk. He described Mars as a spherical body illuminated by the Sun. For more than 200 years after that, no astronomer managed to detect any significant details on the planet's surface, although Giovanni Cassini did note changes in the size of the polar caps and calculated the planet's rotation period to be around 24 hours. Telescopic exploration of Mars took a more interesting turn in 1869, when Angelo Secchi succeeded in drawing the planet's surface, and showed dark lines upon it which he termed *canali*, or channels.

Tales of Martians

In 1887, the astronomer Giovanni Schiaparelli observed Mars with a 20-inch (49 cm) telescope and noted the *canali* for himself. The term was translated into English as "canals" and immediately led to the popular notion that these constructions had been built by some form of intelligent life. The story of a Martian civilization spread around the world like wildfire. Meanwhile, in 1877, Asaph Hall discovered the planet's two satellites, Phobos and Deimos, two asteroids a few kilometers across that had been captured into Martian orbit. Excitement about intelligent life on Mars reached fever pitch at the beginning of the twentieth century, when the American astronomer Percival Lowell, with a 24-inch (60 cm) telescope specially constructed for the purpose, made a detailed map of Mars complete with an intricate system of canals. Under the influence of H.G. Wells's *The War of the Worlds*, just published, and impressed by the achievements of the canal-building age (the Suez, Corinth, and Panama canals were opened in 1869, 1893, and 1914 respectively), Lowell depicted Mars as a planet whose equatorial zones were deserts. So dry

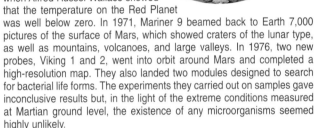

Percival Lowell's impression of the Martian canals. ▷

were they, thought Lowell, that the planet's inhabitants had to build canals to irrigate them. What was more, the seasonal color variations convinced him that there was abundant vegetation on Mars. Percival Lowell's Martians finally lost credibility in 1907, when Alfred Russel Wallace showed that the temperature on the Red Planet was well below zero. In 1971, Mariner 9 beamed back to Earth 7,000 pictures of the surface of Mars, which showed craters of the lunar type, as well as mountains, volcanoes, and large valleys. In 1976, two new probes, Viking 1 and 2, went into orbit around Mars and completed a high-resolution map. They also landed two modules designed to search for bacterial life forms. The experiments they carried out on samples gave inconclusive results but, in the light of the extreme conditions measured at Martian ground level, the existence of any microorganisms seemed highly unlikely.

However, there was a new development 20 years later, when in July 1996 a NASA research team announced the discovery of fossilized life forms in a meteorite that fell to Earth 13,000 years ago. They believed that this rock had been flung from Mars 16 million years before, by the impact of a large meteorite. These results are still being treated with the greatest caution, since it is not possible to prove whether the traces of carbon that were found came from fossilized microorganisms, or are simply the products of a chemical process.

In July 1997, the unmanned Mars Pathfinder craft landed on Mars to explore the region around a dried-up flood channel, using a mobile robot. One month later, the Mars Global Surveyor went into orbit around the planet and sent back an even more detailed map of its surface than the one obtained by Viking.

◁ *Ares Vallis, the site of an ancient flash flood channel, where the Mars Pathfinder probe landed at the spot marked with an X.*

Mars

OBSERVING MARS

Mars is easily distinguished from all the other planets by its pronounced reddish color. But although it is a close neighbor of our own planet, it is a difficult object to observe with a telescope. Except for its periods of opposition, the times when it is closest to Earth, it appears as a tiny, orange-tinted disk on which it is difficult to make out any features.

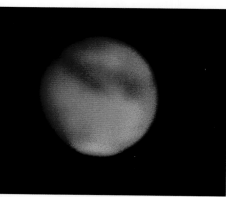

△ Mars as seen from Earth with a telescope.

To observe Mars successfully (or at least to have a good chance of doing so), it is best is to wait for an opposition. These occur every two years, but the conditions for observation can vary widely. In March 1997, for example, the apparent diameter of the planet was scarcely 14.2″, while in April 1999 it was 16.2″, and in June 2001 it was as much as 20.8″.

An important opposition took place in August 2003, when Mars passed by the Earth at a distance of only 56 million kilometers, with an apparent diameter of 25.1″. But even without such ideal conditions, during any opposition a 2¹/₂-inch (60 mm) telescope will show the polar caps and some of the more prominent topographical features. With a larger instrument 4 to 8 inches (100 to 200 mm) in diameter, using a magnification of ×150 to ×200 and aided by a map of the planet's surface, it becomes possible to identify most of the dark regions, such as Syrtis Major, Utopia, or Mare Acidalium. The variations in the extent of the Martian polar caps can also be detected.

Observing Mars is a tricky business, and your first glimpse of the planet in a telescope may reveal nothing but a small reddish-brown disk. You need both patience and practice if you are to succeed in studying its

RETROGRADE MOTION

In the months just before and after an opposition, Mars appears to stop and then move backwards for a while in relation to the stars, before moving forward again. This apparent retrograde motion is an optical effect due to the relative positions of Mars and Earth. The other outer planets also have periods of retrograde motion.

surface in detail. After a few minutes' concentration, however, you will begin to make out color variations on the planet's surface. The observation of Mars is excellent practice for the study of all the other planets.

△ *The Martian landscape viewed by the Mars Pathfinder. In the foreground is the Sojourner robot, which explored the surrounding area.*

The principal features of Mars

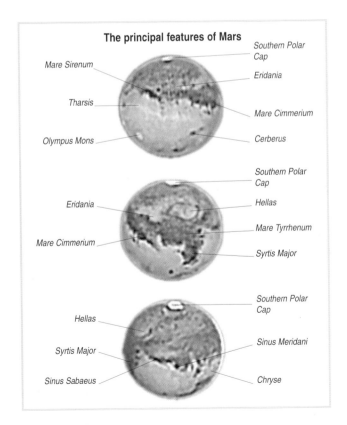

Mare Sirenum

Tharsis

Olympus Mons

Southern Polar Cap

Eridania

Mare Cimmerium

Cerberus

Eridania

Mare Cimmerium

Southern Polar Cap

Hellas

Mare Tyrrhenum

Syrtis Major

Hellas

Syrtis Major

Sinus Sabaeus

Southern Polar Cap

Sinus Meridani

Chryse

THE ASTEROID BELT

WITNESSES TO THE PAST

The region known to astronomers as the Asteroid belt lies between Mars and Jupiter. It consists of innumerable planet-like objects forming a sort of ring. The largest of these, Ceres, is an approximate sphere with a diameter of 940 kilometers, while the smallest are irregularly shaped pieces of debris just a few dozen meters across.

The term "ring" should not be taken to mean that the Asteroid belt is densely packed with rocks in frequent collision with one another. On average, each large asteroid is separated from its nearest neighbor by about 5 million kilometers and, although there are occasional collisions, they only happen once every 100,000 years or so.

The Asteroid belt lies between 2 and 4 AU from the Sun, in a region of the Solar System where it was impossible for a planet to form because of the disruptive influence of nearby Jupiter. For this reason, astronomers believe that many of the rocky objects found here are among the oldest in the Solar System, dating from a time before the planets had come into existence. Up to roughly 4,500 million years ago, only small rocky bodies orbited the Sun. Beyond a distance of 3 AU they consisted predominantly of ice rather than rock, due to the low temperature. But at a distance of less than 3 AU the ice melted, leaving only pieces of mineral debris which collected to form small planetoid bodies: the asteroids. Most of them were drawn toward bodies larger than themselves, the protoplanets, which acted like gigantic vacuum cleaners, clearing the space around them of asteroids – except between Mars and Jupiter. For this reason, a number of the rocks there can bear witness to the conditions that prevailed over 4,500 million years ago in the vicinity of the Sun.

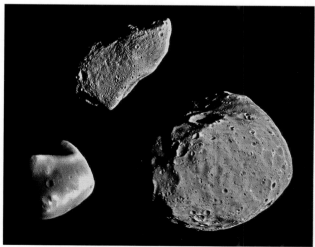

△ Deimos (l) and Phobos (r), two asteroids captured by Mars, shown with Gaspra (top).

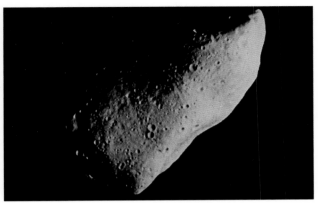

△ *Gaspra was the first asteroid to be observed close up, by the Galileo probe.*

But not all the asteroids are as ancient as this, and astronomers have discovered significant variations in their composition. Approximately 60% of them (known as type C asteroids) probably date from the era when the Solar System was formed. The others are either rocky (type S) or metallic (type M), and owe their existence to the break-up of larger objects, probably with a diameter of more than 200 kilometers. This is the minimum size at which an object's own gravity generates sufficient internal heat to give rise to differentiated layers: heavy elements in the magma, such as metals, are drawn to the center to form a core, while the lighter elements, such as silicates, float to the surface to form a mantle. Following a collision, an object like this would disintegrate, pieces of its

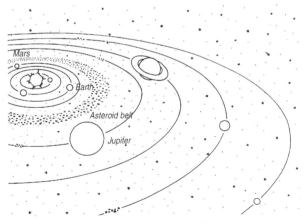

△ *Most asteroids are found in a belt between Mars and Jupiter.*

The Asteroid Belt

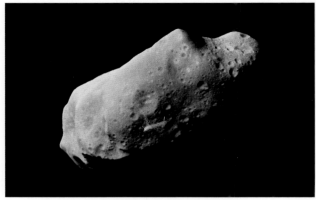

△ *Ida is a rocky object 52 kilometers long and has a small satellite, Dactyl, orbiting it at a distance of 100 kilometers.*

core forming type M asteroids and debris from its mantle becoming type S asteroids.

Some of these minor planets revolve in individual orbits that are a long way from the Asteroid belt. Drawn off course by the major planets, a few occasionally pass close by Earth. The largest of these, Eros, is an object shaped like an American or rugby football measuring 14 × 14 × 40 km. Another is Adonis, familiar because of its role in the Tintin adventure *Explorers on the Moon*, and Phobos and Deimos, the two Martian moons, were captured by the planet when they ventured outside the Asteroid belt. A similar fate must account for Jupiter's outer satellites.

There are about 500 asteroids sharing Jupiter's orbit around the Sun, preceding or following the planet at an angle of 60°. These are known as the Trojans, and named after heroes of the Trojan War.

HISTORY AND DISCOVERIES

At the end of the eighteenth century, several astronomers were trying to prove the Titius–Bode law, which sought to establish a relationship between the distances of the planets from the Sun (see p.75). There seemed to be a gap between Mars and Jupiter, until Giuseppe Piazzi discovered the asteroid Ceres here in 1801. But, being less than 1,000 kilometers in diameter, Ceres proved something of a disappointment to astronomers hoping to find a new planet. Other small planetoid bodies were discovered in the same region: Pallas (discovered in 1802), Juno (1804), and Vesta (1807) were just the first in a list that today runs to many thousands.

Until the beginning of the twentieth century, astronomers thought these bodies might be the remains of a planet destroyed in a massive collision, but in fact it seems that they never succeeded in consolidating into one or more planets. In 1991, the US space probe Galileo, en route to Jupiter, succeeded for the first time in photographing an asteroid at close quarters. Named Gaspra, it had been discovered by telescope in 1916. It was irregularly shaped, 20 × 12 kilometers in size, and pitted with impact craters. These enabled scientists to date its surface, which was around 500 million years old.

Two years later, the same spacecraft flew close to Ida, an asteroid 52 kilometers long, and to the astonishment of scientists it turned out to have its own satellite, an object 1.5 kilometers in diameter which was given the name Dactyl. In June 1997, the NEAR probe, on a mission to orbit Eros, photographed Matilda, an oval body in the Asteroid belt about the same size as Ida.

OBSERVING ASTEROIDS

Although asteroids can be observed with a telescope, they are difficult to distinguish from stars: because of their small size they look like dots, even with strong magnification. The larger ones can also be found with binoculars if their exact position is known, but a good sky map is essential for this, as asteroids change their position among the stars from one day to the next.

This is about as far as amateur astronomers can go. Some observers equipped with CCD cameras have succeeded in recording fluctuations in the brightness of certain asteroids, thereby determining their period of rotation. Others have managed to find new ones, using long CCD exposures. But only the most accomplished and dedicated of amateur astronomers can achieve results like this.

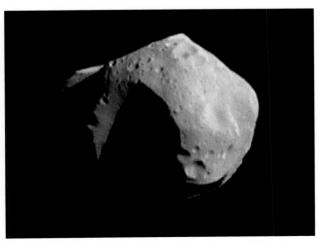

△ The asteroid Matilda. The collision that caused the massive crater 20 kilometers across on its surface must have nearly destroyed it.

JUPITER

THE GIANT OF THE SOLAR SYSTEM

Jupiter is such a large planet that it is tempting to compare it to a star that failed to ignite. Unlike Earth, Mercury, Venus, or Mars, Jupiter has no rocky surface, but is a gigantic ball of gas. For a spacecraft to land on its surface would be impossible, and a good analogy would be to imagine an airplane descending through the clouds. But Jupiter's gases do not burn and produce light like those of the Sun and, though it is very heavy for a planet, Jupiter is not nearly massive enough to produce the thermo-nuclear reactions at its core that would turn it into a star. It would need to have at least 80 times its actual mass to become a brown dwarf, one of the smallest types of star in the Galaxy.

The world of Jupiter is totally different from our own, though its history began at the same time as Earth's and in a similar way, some 4,500 million years ago. The Sun was still surrounded by the nebula from which it had just formed. In the disk of gas and dust revolving around the Sun, solid bodies of greater and greater size had begun to accumulate, gradually turning into protoplanets. At distances of less than 3 AU from the Sun, the heat which it radiated prevented ice from existing in solid form, allowing only silicates and metals to collect and form the cores of rocky planets such as Earth and Mars. Beyond 3 AU from the Sun, in addition to silicates and metals, more volatile substances (such as water, methane, and ammonia) remained in

Gaseous hydrogen
Very dense core
Metallic hydrogen

△ The structure of Jupiter

solid form. This additional material allowed larger planetoid cores to form – that of Jupiter being approximately 10 times larger than that of Earth – and these heavy cores, in their turn, attracted further matter from the nebula surrounding the Sun. Over many hundreds of millions of years, Jupiter sucked in all the surrounding gas to become the vast gaseous sphere we see today. The planet's rocky core represents only 0.03% of its total mass: the rest consists of hydrogen (90%) and helium (10%), with traces of water vapor, methane, ammonia, and ammonium hydrosulfite.

Journey to the Center of Jupiter

A voyage toward the heart of the giant planet has already been made by a small module released from the Galileo space probe in December 1995. Suspended from a parachute, the device descended through the outer layers of cloud until it was destroyed by the planet's atmospheric pressure when this reached 24 times the pressure on Earth. A hypothetical device capable of resisting even more extreme conditions, continuing the descent, would find that the atmosphere became increasingly dense. The hydrogen would liquefy and then, 8,500 kilometers below the cloud tops, it would be compressed to the point where it became metallic in form (hydrogen possesses the same conducting properties as metals). The pressure here would be in excess of two million Earth atmospheres, and the temperature 10,000°C. At 57,000 kilometers below the cloud tops, the original core of the planet is subjected to a pressure of 45 million atmospheres and heated to 30,000°C.

This intense heat, augmented by the Sun's radiation, is thought to be responsible for the cloud movements observed on Jupiter. Winds with speeds of 180 meters per second have been measured on the planet, although Jupiter's local weather systems are still not fully understood. Its Great Red Spot, in particular, remains a mystery. For over 150 years, this enormous anticyclonic whirlwind, larger than Earth itself, has existed in the atmosphere of Jupiter. How it evolved is unknown, as is the reason

△ Jupiter, seen with two of its principal moons, Io and Europa.

Jupiter

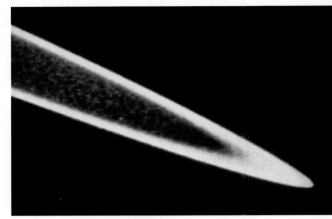

△ Jupiter's rings, discovered by Voyager 1 in 1979.

for its red coloration.

Like Saturn, Jupiter possesses a system of rings, but they are extremely tenuous and were only discovered in 1979 by the Voyager 1 space probe. They cannot be detected by observers on Earth using the visible wavelengths of the spectrum.

Io, Europa, Ganymede, and Callisto

Jupiter has four large moons. Io, the closest to the planet, is studded with active volcanoes that constantly eject sulfur into space. Though it is too small to have its own internal source of energy (it is only 3,630 kilometers in diameter), Io is so close to its parent planet (422,000 kilometers up) that it is permanently subjected to flexing by the tidal forces of Jupiter, heating it and keeping its volcanoes active.

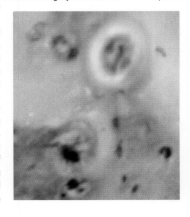

Europa, the smallest of Jupiter's moons (3,138 kilometers in diameter), is likewise subject to the influence of the planet's tides, but since it is further away (671,000 kilometers up) and entirely covered in ice, their effects on Europa are different. On close-up pictures obtained from space probes, the surface of Europa looks like a gigantic ice floe floating in a liquid ocean. This coating of ice is fractured into hundreds of plates which move against each other under the influence of Jupiter's tides. In all probability, geysers of liquid water from the ocean beneath gush out from time to time at the joint between two plates.

Ganymede is the largest of the Galilean moons, and it too is covered in ice. It may also have a liquid ocean beneath the surface crust. Finally, Callisto, the most distant, appears to have been petrified ever since its formation 4,500 million years ago.

Twelve other satellites orbit Jupiter, but these are not the only bodies accompanying it on its journey round the Sun. At two specific points on Jupiter's orbit known as Lagrangian points, 60° behind and 60° ahead of the planet in its path around the Sun, lie clusters of small bodies called Trojans, which are similar to asteroids.

▽ *An erupting volcano on the surface of Io.*

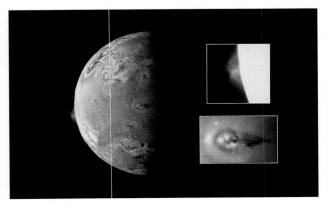

HISTORY AND DISCOVERIES

In 1610, Galileo became the first person to observe Jupiter with a telescope. Since then, the four principal satellites which he discovered have been known collectively as the Galilean moons. In 1664, the

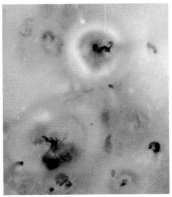

◁ *These two pictures of Io, taken 17 years apart, show how volcanic activity is continually reshaping its surface.*

Jupiter

English scientist Robert Hooke noted features on Jupiter's surface. In the following year, Giovanni Cassini became the first to observe the principal cloud belts covering the planet, and in 1831, Heinrich Schwabe discovered the immense anticyclone known as the Great Red Spot, which has remained active ever since.

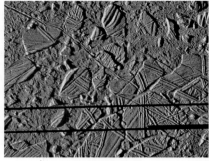

△ *The cracked ice floe forming Europa's surface probably conceals a liquid ocean beneath.*

Telescopic observation continued to be the only means of studying the planet until 1955, when astronomers discovered that Jupiter was a powerful source of radio signals. Then came the space probes, of which five have so far visited the planet. In 1973, Pioneer 10 measured Jupiter's intense magnetic field, although it was as much as one million kilometers away. The following year, Pioneer 11 took close-up pictures of the Great Red Spot and of the polar regions. In 1979, the two Voyager spacecraft unveiled many of the planet's secrets by producing the first high-resolution images of Jupiter and its moons. Active volcanoes were observed on Io and new satellites were discovered. Finally, in December 1995, Galileo became the first spacecraft to go into orbit around the planet, releasing a module into Jupiter's atmosphere and analyzing its composition. Despite a fault in the craft's principal transmitting antenna, it sent back to Earth the closest ever views of the Galilean moons. Just before this, in July 1994, astronomers had been lucky enough to watch fragments of Comet Shoemaker–Levy 9 colliding with the planet. Blocks of ice around a kilometer in diameter smashed into it, with devastating effects that could easily be seen with telescopes on Earth.

OBSERVING JUPITER

Jupiter is easy to find with the naked eye, even if you do not know beforehand in which part of the sky to look. After Venus, it is the brightest object in the sky. Late at night, if the brightest star you can see shines steadily without twinkling, then it is not a star at all: it is Jupiter. It can only be confused with Venus when it is near the setting Sun in the evening, or near the rising Sun at daybreak. At these times, a pair of binoculars with ×10 magnification will decide the matter by showing the Galilean moons quite plainly. Even this low magnification is enough to reveal Jupiter as a planet, not a mere pinpoint in the sky as it appears to the naked eye. On the other hand, you will not be able to see the clouds surrounding the planet in any detail.

Although it is never much less than 600 million kilometers away, Jupiter is easy for amateur astronomers to observe, as it is a gigantic sphere 11.2 times the diameter of Earth. A detailed view of the planet can be obtained with a relatively small telescope. A 2½-inch (60 mm) refractor will show the two main belts of cloud encircling it and, in ideal conditions, other belts will also be visible. The Great Red Spot will be invisible, however, chiefly because it does not contrast strongly with other cloud formations. After a few minutes' observation, you will be able to detect the movement of the four Galilean moons. You may even observe a satellite being eclipsed by the planet's shadow, or see one of them passing across its face. However, when this happens, the moon's shadow projected onto the clouds will be too small to detect. Astronomical tables published each month in specialist journals show the moons' positions each day, enabling the observer to work out in advance precisely when to look for these phenomena.

A 4-inch (100 mm) instrument is large enough to enable you to find the Great Red Spot and pick out lesser meteorological features in the cloud belts. It also makes the shadows of Jupiter's moons in their passage across its surface just detectable, though not without difficulty. In July 1994, the effects of the impact of Shoemaker–Levy 9 were clearly visible with instruments of this size.

With a telescope 6 inches (150 mm) or more in diameter, detailed study of the planet becomes possible. Irregularities in the surface of the cloud belts can be seen. The many spots can be used as reference points for watching a complete rotation of the planet on its axis in under 10 hours, a suitable project for a long winter night. The passage of the moons across Jupiter is easily observed with a telescope over 6 inches (150 mm).

△ In 1994, fragments of Comet Shoemaker–Levy 9 disintegrated in Jupiter's atmosphere, producing these large dark patches.

◁ The Great Red Spot is a giant anticyclone (high pressure area) that has persisted for over 150 years.

SATURN

THE RINGED PLANET

Like Jupiter, Saturn is a huge gaseous sphere, a planet upon which it would be quite impossible to land. Clouds of various colors form its visible surface. A spacecraft attempting to explore Saturn would pass straight through it, to start with at least, for the planet consists of a layer of gaseous hydrogen 30,000 kilometers thick which gradually gives way to a lower layer of metallic hydrogen, like the interior of Jupiter. The atmospheric pressure increases to 2 million times the pressure at sea level on Earth, raising the temperature to 8,000°C. At the planet's center is a rocky core about 30,000 kilometers across, which is less than a quarter of Saturn's total diameter, heated to around 15,000°C. Although Saturn's mass is 95 times that of Earth, it is still a "light" planet, since it is less dense than water. In other words, if there were a large enough sea in the Universe, Saturn would float upon it.

△ A view of Saturn from Voyager 2.

Storms on Saturn

The atmosphere on Saturn consists of 88% hydrogen and 10% helium, the remaining 2% being a mixture of methane, ammonia, ammonium hydrosulfite, and water. Astronomers have observed that every 30 years an enormous storm is unleashed upon its surface, spreading rapidly over the entire planet with winds that can reach 1,800 kilometers per hour. There is no phenomenon like it anywhere else in the Solar System, and it always occurs in a period corresponding to the middle of the planet's summer. Although its cause is unknown, seasonal factors could well play a part.

△ Saturn's clouds as seen by Voyager 2.

Apart from these disturbances, the atmosphere on Saturn appears very calm. The clouds are arranged in colored belts, though these are seen less distinctly than those on Jupiter, probably because a covering layer of ammonia softens their colors. But even when there are no storms, the winds are generally much stronger than those on Jupiter.

Like the other planets, Saturn was formed some 4,500 million years ago. It began in exactly the same way as Jupiter, with the accumulation of a large core of ice and rock, whose mass was sufficient to attract nearby hydrogen and helium that had been part of the Sun's enveloping nebula. These gases now make up the dense atmosphere of Saturn. From the top of its highest clouds, the planet's encircling rings would be clearly visible as a gigantic arch stretching right across the sky. But this would only be true from a vantage point close to Saturn's equator: because of the planet's curvature, the rings (even though they are some 280,000 kilometers in diameter) would be permanently hidden below the horizon for an observer near the poles. However, the rings can be plainly seen from Earth with a small

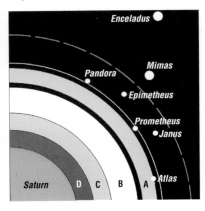

◁ A diagram showing the arrangement of Saturn's rings and the distances of its closest satellites.

Saturn

◁ *The angle of Saturn's rings changes over the years, as shown by this series of pictures taken by the Hubble Space Telescope (top), and by the French Pic du Midi observatory. In the bottom image, the rings are seen precisely edge on, and seem to have disappeared.*

astronomical telescope. They look smooth and symmetrical, but are in fact composed of a huge number of icy particles, and it is the highly reflective quality of water ice that is responsible for the rings' great brightness. The smallest particles are no more than dust, while the largest are probably just a few meters across. All this debris revolves around Saturn like so many miniature satellites. It is astonishing to think that this brightly shining disk is only about thirty meters thick. The rings are also slightly warped, like a bicycle wheel that has been in an accident, with the result that, as it turns, the disk wobbles from edge to edge with an amplitude of 5 kilometers.

The origin of the rings is still uncertain, and astronomers have advanced two theories. The first supposes that the particles that constitute the rings failed to form into satellites, which would make them very old, predating the formation of the planets. They never accreted to form satellites because they were too close to the planet. In fact, the densest part of the rings (visible with a telescope from Earth) is less than 140,000 kilometers from the center of Saturn, and this distance corresponds precisely to the so-called Roche limit, within which a planet's tidal forces prevent any cohesive bodies from forming. The second theory posits a small planet that was captured by Saturn relatively recently. Dragged down below the Roche limit, the planet would have disintegrated and its debris spread into rings separated by "empty" spaces, the most prominent of which are the

Cassini and Encke divisions. Around the outer edge of the dense rings, in 1995, astronomers observed "ephemeral satellites," blocks of ice forming a partial ring that seemed to be trying to coalesce and form a satellite. But their proximity to the Roche limit and the disruptive influence of satellites in nearby orbits dispersed them again. Astronomers think that phenomena of this kind may be recurrent features at the outer edge of Saturn's rings.

Beyond the densest rings, Saturn is orbited by satellites, as well as further, faint rings which are invisible from Earth. Some of the satellites share the same orbit, such as Telesto, Tethys, and Calypso, or Dione and Helene. Largest of them all is Titan, with a diameter of 5,150 kilometers. Larger than Mercury, this satellite is unusual in being covered by a dense, opaque atmosphere with a surface pressure 1.6 times greater than at sea level on Earth. Its frozen surface (at −183°C) may have continents covered in viscous tar and surrounded by seas of methane. It may even snow or rain methane in places. Titan is still one of the most mysterious places in the entire Solar System.

HISTORY AND DISCOVERIES

Saturn is the most distant planet to have been known since Antiquity, but it was not until 1610 that its nature began to be understood, when Galileo observed the planet through his telescope. To him, Saturn was a body just like the Moon, Jupiter, Venus, or the Earth. But he was worried by two earlike protuberances that stood out from either side of it. At first he took them for two satellites, but he quickly discovered that, unlike Jupiter's moons, they did not appear to move round the planet. Two years later, he was disconcerted to find they had disappeared. We now know that what he saw was the planet's rings, which appear to vanish when they are viewed edge on.

The mystery was only solved in 1654 by Christiaan Huygens, who realized that Saturn was encircled by a ring running round its equator.

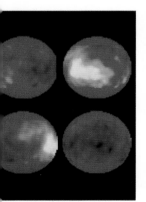

Soon afterwards, Giovanni Cassini observed that the ring was not continuous: it was interrupted by an empty strip, which we now know as the Cassini division. In 1857, James Clerk Maxwell put forward the theory that the rings were not rigid structures, but were composed of a multitude of small satellites. His hypothesis was not confirmed until 1895,

◁ *The Hubble Space Telescope took these infrared photographs of Titan, in which vague shapes can be glimpsed through its dense covering of cloud.*

Saturn

when the American astronomer James Keeler demonstrated with the aid of a spectrum that the rings revolved round Saturn at different speeds. This is exactly how one would expect an immense crowd of small satellites to behave.

In 1979, Pioneer 11 was the first space probe to approach Saturn, and it discovered a new ring (designated by the letter E) outside the others. The following year, the Voyager 1 and 2 missions showed that there are actually thousands of thin ringlets. At the same time, the principal satellites were photographed at close quarters. Meanwhile, as our own planet passed through the same plane as the rings, other small satellites were discovered by observers on Earth: Atlas, Prometheus, Epimetheus, Telesto, Calypso, and Helene.

OBSERVING SATURN

Identifying Saturn with the unaided eye is a process of elimination. Like the other planets, it appears in the sky as a star that does not twinkle. If a planet is very white and bright near the setting Sun at nightfall, or near the rising Sun before daybreak, it is probably Venus. If it shines very brightly in the middle of the night, it is Jupiter. If

△ *Saturn viewed through a small telescope such as an amateur might use.*

it is red in color, it is Mars. But if it is none of these, then it is Saturn. It is best to consult a set of astronomical tables to find out approximately where to look for it and at what time.

A small refractor 2 to 2¹/₂ inches (50 to 60 mm) in diameter, fitted with

△ *An artist's impression of Saturn's rings.*

△ *The great storm of 1990, detected by the Pic du Midi observatory and photographed by the Hubble Space Telescope.*

a ×30 or ×35 eyepiece, is quite large enough to start exploring the ringed planet. The image may be small, but it is probably much better than the one Galileo had to make do with. To realize this is to understand instantly why Galileo found the protuberances formed by the rings around Saturn so difficult to interpret. Titan is also discernible with an instrument of this size. A 4-inch (100 mm) telescope with ×100 magnification will reveal more detail, notably the Cassini division, a dark band separating the bright A and B rings. The shadow of the planet on its rings and the shadow of the rings on the planet can also be seen if conditions are favorable. An instrument 6 to 8 inches (150 to 200 mm) in diameter is needed to study the clouds on Saturn, although the contrasting colors in the planet's atmosphere will still not show up very clearly.

Apart from Titan, the only satellites an amateur observer may hope to detect are Iapetus, Rhea, Dione, and Tethys, though none of these is easy to locate, especially Iapetus. Every fifteen years, because they are at an angle of 27° to the orbital plane of the planet, Saturn's rings seem to disappear. In fact, observers on Earth are simply viewing them edge on, and since they are extremely thin, they become invisible. This phenomenon last occurred in 1995 and is expected again in 2009.

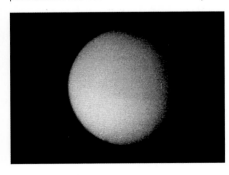

◁ *Titan, viewed here from a Voyager space probe, remains shrouded in its dense atmosphere.*

URANUS

SUMMER AT THE POLES

Uranus is a planet of the same type as Jupiter and Saturn, a gaseous sphere without a firm surface. It is smaller than either of them, and also much further from the Sun (at an approximate distance of 3,000 million kilometers). Because it receives much less heat from the Sun and its surface temperature is correspondingly lower, it has dense clouds of methane, which would be impossible on Saturn and Jupiter. It is the presence of methane that gives Uranus its distinctive blue-green tint.

Although the planet was formed at the same time and in the same way

△ *Miranda, the smallest of the principal moons of Uranus, is only 480 km in diameter, and its strangely jumbled surface is suggestive of violent activity.*

as Saturn, its axis of rotation is markedly different, for instead of being perpendicular it is more or less parallel to the plane of its orbit. This peculiar tilt probably resulted from a collision with another planet the size of Earth. If so, its satellites must have tilted with it, since they revolve around Uranus in equatorial orbits. But it is also possible that Uranus's sideways progress through the Solar System is due to gravitational disturbance from the other planets.

HISTORY AND DISCOVERIES

On March 13, 1781, when he saw Uranus for the first time in his 6½-inch (160 mm) telescope, the British astronomer William Herschel thought it was a comet. He was observing the sky in the constellation Gemini when

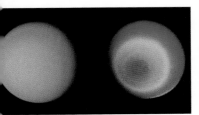

△ *Close-up views of Uranus taken by Voyager 2 in 1986.*

by chance he noticed a new and strangely diffuse object. Though he tried using stronger and stronger magnification, he could make out nothing more than a small, fuzzy disk. He had to make further observations before he could calculate its orbit and confirm that it was indeed a planet, situated beyond Saturn. Its great distance makes Uranus very difficult to observe with a telescope. However, as early as 1787 Herschel discovered two satellites, which were named Titania and Oberon. In 1851, William Lassell added to the picture by detecting two more moons of lesser size, Ariel and Umbriel. It was only in 1948 that Gerard Kuiper first saw Miranda, a small satellite very close to its parent planet.

On March 10, 1977, during the occultation of a star by Uranus, astronomers noticed that there were rings around the planet, just like those encircling Saturn, but much thinner. In January 1986, the US space probe Voyager 2 succeeded in taking the first – and still the only – close-up pictures of Uranus and its moons. The probe revealed ten other satellites in addition to the five already known, and others were found in the 1990s.

OBSERVING URANUS

With a magnitude of only 5.5 at its brightest, Uranus is near the limit of visibility with the unaided eye. In theory, the planet should be visible with binoculars, but the problem is locating it. In a telescope with a low-magnification eyepiece, Uranus appears as a bright spot that is difficult to distinguish from the surrounding stars. The task is easier if your instrument has a mount that allows you to pinpoint the planet by its coordinates. Even then, patience and a good sky atlas are both required if you are to track it down successfully. With a magnification of ×100 to ×200, Uranus looks like a tiny, blue-green, blurred disk, with no detail visible. Its apparent diameter is only in the region of 4″.

Even with a powerful telescope, Uranus remains a small and featureless sphere, difficult to locate. Although this picture was taken by the Voyager 2 probe, it gives an idea of what Uranus looks like in a telescope. ▷

NEPTUNE

DATA

Eighth Planet from the Sun
Average Distance from the Sun: 30.06 AU
Sidereal Revolution Period: 164 years, 288 days
Sidereal Rotation Period: 16h 07m
Oblateness: 0.017
Axial Inclination: 28°
Diameter: 49,528 km (3.9 times that of Earth)
Volume: 58 times that of Earth
Mass: 17 times that of Earth
Temperature at Cloud Tops: −220°C
Satellites: 8

THE SECOND BLUE PLANET

Neptune is the outermost of the four gaseous planets in the Solar System, and the smallest of them. It was formed in the same way as Jupiter, Saturn, and Uranus. Its blue atmosphere is a mixture of hydrogen, helium, methane, and ammonia. Because of its great distance (4,500 million kilometers), Neptune receives little of the Sun's energy, and the low temperatures might lead one to suppose that it is a relatively tranquil world. But Voyager 2, the only space probe to have got near the planet, sent back pictures of turbulent cloud formations recalling those seen on Jupiter. The strongest winds in the Solar System have been detected on Neptune, with speeds of up to 2,200 kilometers per hour. A large dark spot was also observed. Like the Great Red Spot on Jupiter, it was actually an enormous anticyclone about the size of the Earth. It was located at latitude 22° south and took 18 hours 20 minutes to sweep round the planet. A smaller dark spot located at latitude 55° south circled the planet in 16 hours 50 minutes. High up, 50 kilometers above the other clouds, wispy cirrus clouds of ammonia were seen to drift across the face of Neptune. Like the three other so-called Jovian planets, Neptune possesses a system of rings, but it differs from the others in that, rather than being homogeneous, the rings contain arcs of matter much denser than the rest. The planet has four principal rings and eight satellites. Its largest satellite is Triton, an ice-covered sphere 2,706 kilometers in diameter which circles Neptune in a retrograde orbit. This suggests that the satellite was originally captured by Neptune. It is falling inexorably

◁ *Neptune seen in close-up by the Voyager 2 probe.*

toward the planet and, in 100 million years' time, will cross the Roche limit (the nearest an object in space can get to another before the smaller one breaks up), which spells the beginning of its end. Eventually it will become another of Neptune's rings. Mysterious geysers of dark gas sometimes erupt on Triton, spouting up to eight kilometers high.

HISTORY AND DISCOVERIES

Neptune is invisible to the naked eye and was the first planet to be discovered not by chance, but as the result of calculations. In 1845, François Arago, director of the Paris Observatory, asked his colleague Urbain Le Verrier to study the movement of Uranus, which nobody could either understand or predict. Le Verrier quickly worked out that the irregularities in its orbit could be attributed to the presence of a massive planet more than 30 AU from the Sun. Having checked his figures, Le Verrier asked Johann Galle, of the Berlin Observatory, to search for this hypothetical planet in the region where his computations said it would be. After two nights of searching, on September 24, 1846, the German astronomer announced that he had indeed found it, 52' away from its predicted

△ The frozen surface of Triton

position. Just seventeen days later, William Lassell became the first person to observe Triton, the largest of Neptune's moons. Working independently of Le Verrier, a young Englishman named John Couch Adams had reached the same conclusions, but could find nobody willing to confirm them by undertaking a search. Since that time, the study of Neptune, which is still a difficult planet to observe, has revealed few new facts. In 1984 and 1985, during occultations of stars by

Neptune, André Brahic and Bruno Sicardy of France discovered the planet to be surrounded by a system of partial rings, or arcs. In 1989, the Voyager 2 space probe came very close to Neptune, and discovered six new satellites in addition to Triton and Nereid.

OBSERVING NEPTUNE

Neptune, with a magnitude of 7.9, can be observed with telescopes under 4 inches (100 mm) in diameter. The difficulty is locating it and distinguishing it from surrounding stars. Patience and a good sky atlas are the keys to success. By observing over two nights, you will be able to detect the planet's movement among the stars, which is one way of solving the problem. But once a likely candidate has been located, you will need to use stronger magnification for the object to lose its dotlike appearance. In an instrument of over 4 inches (100 mm) and ×200 magnification, Neptune appears as a small bluish disk, although no detail is visible.

PLUTO

TERRA INCOGNITA

In 2007, Pluto lost its status as planet and was categorized as a dwarf planet (or planetoid). To this day, Pluto has not been visited by a space probe. Even when viewed with the most powerful telescopes on Earth, it remains a small speck in the sky, but with the help of the Hubble Space Telescope, astronomers have managed to distinguish a few vague marks on its surface. Even without close examination, however, we know Pluto to be a frozen world, perhaps like Triton (one of Neptune's moons), whose surface is probably composed mostly of crystallized nitrogen. Pluto has an extremely tenuous atmosphere (its pressure is 100,000 times weaker than at sea level on Earth), consisting predominantly of nitrogen, with traces of methane and carbon monoxide. The atmosphere changes with the dwarf planet's distance from the Sun, which because of Pluto's eccentric orbit varies between 4,000 and 7,000 million kilometers. Between January 21, 1979, and March 14, 1999, Pluto was closer to the Sun than Neptune. From the furthest point of its orbit, the Sun would look just like a large star, a bright dot in the sky. Charon, Pluto's one satellite, is 600 kilometers across and only 19,400 kilometers above the planet, i.e. 5% of the Moon's distance from Earth.

△ The pair of photographs that identified Pluto.

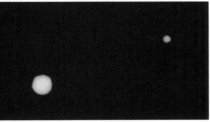

△ *Pluto and its moon, Charon*

HISTORY AND DISCOVERIES

Without realizing it, the American astronomer Percival Lowell, who was searching for a ninth planet beyond Neptune, succeeded in photographing the dwarf planet Pluto. In 1930, Clyde Tombaugh, an amateur astronomer who was also looking for the unknown planet, studied Lowell's photographic plates carefully and noticed a detail that had escaped Lowell himself: on two pictures taken at different times, a "star" had moved – and Pluto was at last discovered.

It was not until 1978 that James Christy discovered that Pluto had a large satellite, christened Charon, which orbited it in 6.39 days and was covered in water ice, but had no atmosphere. Strictly speaking, Pluto–Charon is a double dwarf planet: the two bodies always present the same hemisphere to each other so that, seen from Pluto, Charon remains at a fixed point in the sky. In July 1994, the Hubble Space Telescope succeeded in identifying twelve darker and lighter areas on Pluto's surface. Astronomers will have to make do with this rudimentary map for a long time to come, since no probe is currently planned to explore these distant worlds.

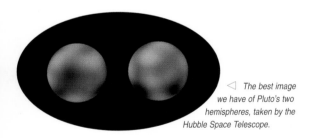

◁ *The best image we have of Pluto's two hemispheres, taken by the Hubble Space Telescope.*

OBSERVING PLUTO

It would be more correct to entitle this paragraph "Not Observing Pluto," for the most distant former planet in the Solar System is never much brighter than magnitude 14. In theory, this calls for a telescope at least 12 inches (300 mm) in diameter, but in practice even that would not be enough. To pick Pluto out among the faint stars surrounding it (even supposing that the telescope is accurately aimed at the dwarf planet), one would have to track its motion, a task probably requiring many nights of observation. The best method is to take photographs in order to detect, just like Clyde Tombaugh in 1930, that something has moved.

COMETS

ICEBERGS IN SPACE

Unlike planets or asteroids, comets are neither rocky nor gaseous. They are irregularly shaped blocks of ice ranging from a few hundred meters to several kilometers in diameter. Their formation predates that of the planets, going back more than 4,500 million years. At that time, the Solar System was still just a disk of gas and dust revolving round a newborn star, the Sun. In the inner regions of this disk, fragments of dust began to accumulate, forming larger and larger bodies. As far out as the orbits of Uranus, Neptune, and Pluto, because of the low temperatures at this great distance from the Sun, the dust fragments became coated with a substantial covering of ice (composed of frozen water or carbon dioxide). These particles adhered to one another to form ever larger lumps, consisting mainly of ice and dust. That is

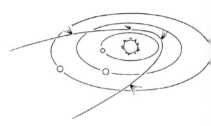

△ *The elongated orbit of a comet brings it close to the Sun at regular intervals.*

the origin of the comets. Some of them were captured by the original cores of the gaseous planets in the course of formation, while others continued their independent journeys through space.

Once the giant planets like Jupiter and Saturn had taken shape, they disrupted the comets' peaceful progress. The gravitational forces they exerted literally hurled the comets into far-off orbits, to distances between 40 and 100,000 AU, taking the comets as far out as halfway to the nearest stars. (Pluto, by comparison, is at a distance of about 40 AU.) The Dutch astronomer Jan Hendrik Oort theorized that many millions of comets inhabit a

During the spring of 1997, Comet Hale–Bopp was visible to the naked eye even in city skies, and was an impressive sight for inhabitants of the northern hemisphere. ▷

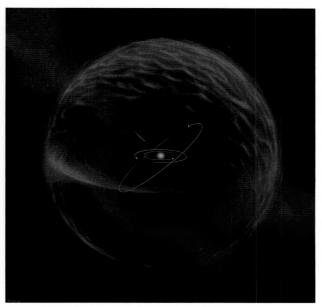

△ *The Oort Cloud and the Kuiper Belt, home of the comets.*

hypothetical structure, now known as the Oort Cloud, which may be the remains of the nebula from which the Solar System was formed, while others lie in the Kuiper Belt, a flat disk extending outwards in the same plane as the planets.

If that were the end of the story, no human being would ever have seen a comet. At a distance of thousands of millions of kilometers, it would be an impossible feat to detect a mere lump of ice. But under the gravitational influence of the nearest stars, some of the comets in the Oort Cloud are deflected from their distant orbits and head for the Sun. They sweep past it only a few hundred million kilometers away, before continuing on their new, elongated orbit. The same happens to some comets from the Kuiper Belt. Although the former only return close to the Sun after several centuries or millennia, the latter come round again after an interval of less than 200 years. The length of time between each perihelion distinguishes short-period from long-period comets.

Even during their periodic visits to the Sun, comets rarely approach it any closer than some tens of millions of kilometers. In 1996, Comet Hyakutake was unusually intrepid, passing only 15 million kilometers from Earth. The following year, the large Comet Hale–Bopp passed by at a more cautious distance of 197 million kilometers. When a comet gets near the Sun, it heats up, and its ice evaporates to form a vast ball of gas up to a million kilometers in diameter. Filled with the dust that was

Comets

△ *Comet Hyakutake, which approached within 15 million kilometers of Earth, was only a few kilometers across.*

imprisoned in the ice, this atmosphere forms the comet's fuzzy coma, which is often visible to the naked eye. The solar wind produced by the Sun's radiation disperses the coma to create the comet's tail. Each time it passes its perihelion, therefore, a comet loses some of its mass.

HISTORY AND DISCOVERIES

Like the Moon and the planets, comets have been known since Antiquity. The Chaldeans, Greeks, Chinese, and Egyptians all recorded the appearance of numerous comets. In the fourth century B.C., Aristotle believed that they originated in the Earth's atmosphere. Their unpredictability led people to think of them as omens of disaster, a belief that persisted into the nineteenth century.

In 1531, Peter Apian noticed that a comet's tail always points away from the Sun. Then, in 1577, the Danish astronomer Tycho Brahe proved that the comets originated from much further away than the distance separating the Moon from the Earth. Finally, in the eighteenth century, Edmond Halley discovered that the comets were bodies belonging to our Solar System and that, like the planets, they moved in orbits around the Sun. The difference was simply that their orbits were much more elongated ellipses, which explained why they appeared so rarely: only every 76 years in the case of the comet that now bears Halley's own name, for example.

But the precise composition of these bodies is still unknown. The earliest spectroscopic analyses, made in the mid-nineteenth century, revealed the presence of carbon, cyanogen, ethylene, and products resulting from the break-up of water molecules. In 1950, the American astronomer Fred Whipple described them as "dirty snowballs." Recent observations, including those made by the European space probe Giotto, which was sent to rendezvous with Halley's Comet in 1986, have confirmed that his description was correct.

OBSERVING COMETS

The most spectacular comets are visible to the naked eye, but these are rare. Each year, on average, professional astronomers observe 25 comets, only a few of which can be seen by amateurs. To search successfully for the less bright comets, an observer needs a thorough knowledge of the night sky. They are easiest to observe with a large diameter telescope, using relatively low magnification. This set-up allows large areas of sky to be scanned, so that any wispy "star" that looks like a blurred spot can be detected more readily.

Comets visible to the unaided eye have included Comet Bennett in 1970, Comet West in 1976, and, more recently, Comets Hyakutake and Hale–Bopp in 1996 and 1997. Halley's Comet, which last returned in 1986, was in theory visible to the naked eye, although in fact it was close to the setting Sun and a pair of good binoculars or a telescope was needed to see it.

To obtain a good view of the brightest comets, and to observe the tail to best advantage, a location free from light pollution is essential. With the aid of binoculars, the head can usually be seen as a small, brilliant spot at the center of the coma. The comet's movement among the stars will be noticeable after watching for several minutes, if it is passing fairly close to the Earth.

With the aid of a telescope, depending on the comet's distance and how active it is, jets of dust and gas may be observed. Changes in these ephemeral objects can be seen from one evening to the next. On rare occasions, pieces break away from the main body, and this phenomenon is sometimes detectable with the equipment available to an amateur.

◁ *Halley's Comet photographed by the Giotto probe: a "dirty snowball" measuring 15 × 8 kilometers.*

THE
CONSTELLATIONS

Constellation name

Best season for observing

CEPHEUS

VISIBLE: all year

The constellation represents Cepheus, king of Ethiopia, husband of Cassiopeia, and father of Andromeda. It lies approximately between Ursa Minor and Cassiopeia.

Cepheus looks rather like a house. To find it, simply extend the line of the two "Pointers" in Ursa Major to Polaris and beyond. ▷

β (Beta) CEPHEI (ALFIRK)

Mag 3.2 & 7.9

This bright star has a companion star of magnitude 7.9, less than 14" away, which can be resolved with a small telescope or binoculars. It was discovered in 1832. Alfirk is a variable star, with a short period (around 4½ hours) but only a slight variation in magnitude.

Diagram caption: gives guidance on locating and observing

Location diagram for the constellation

THESE PAGES

Map

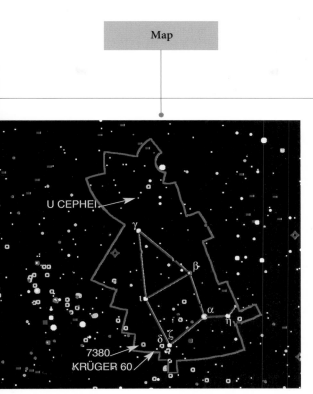

U CEPHEI

γ

β

ι

α

η

δ ζ

7380

KRÜGER 60

ξ (Xi) CEPHEI

Mag
4.5 & 6.5

This star is in fact a physical binary system, the two components of which are only 7.7″ apart. The two stars are at a distance of around 120 light years from Earth.

Designation (Greek name) followed by common name if any

Symbols: magnitude, means of observing, and type of object

HOW TO USE THESE PAGES

Not all of the 88 constellations in the sky are described here; this book is for observers in the northern hemisphere, who cannot see the most southerly ones. Any constellations that never rise above the horizon at latitude 36° north (which is that of the most southerly point in Europe, Gibraltar; or Nashville, Las Vegas, Tokyo, or Beirut) have been omitted.

Nor does the book cover every object in the sky. As a general rule, only those that are easiest to see have been included, but there are exceptions. Some objects are mentioned because they are particularly interesting, although they may be fairly difficult to observe, and in some cases are not easy to find.

CELESTIAL OBJECTS

Apart from the bodies of the Solar System, which move in relation to the stars, all celestial objects stay in the same place, and can therefore be given positions on a map. The following pages give details, constellation by constellation, of many of the stars, nebulae, clusters, and galaxies which may be observed with the naked eye, with binoculars, or with a telescope. A brief description lists their main features (distance, size, etc.), as well how they will appear in each type of instrument.

In some cases, an object that is faint or invisible to the naked eye may be difficult to locate, so, to make the observer's job easier, coordinates are given for these. An instrument equipped with a computerized mount can use the coordinates to locate the object.

LOCATION DIAGRAMS

For each constellation, a small location diagram shows how to find it by using one of the major celestial landmarks, as explained in the chapter "Navigating the Sky." The best time of year for evening observation is also given. To help you to judge the angular distance between stars, you can use the scale on the back cover of this book: when held out at arm's length, 7 inches or 18 centimeters equates to roughly 20° of arc.

Key to the location diagrams:
– red lines: the constellation itself
– black, unbroken lines: other constellations
– broken lines: alignments
– capital letters: constellation names
– lower-case letters: star names

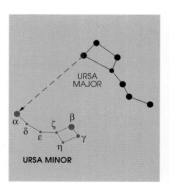

MAPS

As well as all the objects described in the text, the sky maps show some objects which, although not described, serve as navigational aids and help to avoid confusion. This also gives you the opportunity to observe more objects than there is room to describe in this book.

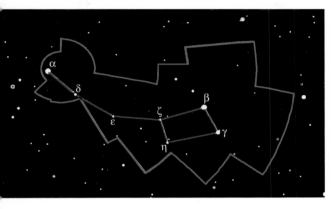

Key to the maps:
– blue lines: the boundaries of the constellation
– red lines: the pattern of the constellation's principal stars
– yellow type: names of the principal stars, and of objects described

Key to map symbols

⬭	**Galaxy**	●	**Globular cluster**
◈	**Planetary nebula**	◉	**Open cluster**
⬡	**Star association**		

NOTE
Overall magnitude and individual magnitude
For objects consisting of a number of bodies, the magnitude given is the object's overall magnitude, which is the sum of the brilliance of all the bodies comprising it. Each body, of course, also has its own individual magnitude.

How to Use these Pages

LOCAL TIME

The times given in this book, both on the seasonal sky maps and to indicate when constellations are visible, are local times. They are valid for observers at any longitude in the northern hemisphere, since the sky seen over, for example, Madrid at 21:00 on a given date is exactly the same as the sky seen over New York or Salt Lake City at 21:00 on the same date. During the summer months, however, adjustment must be made for "daylight saving time" or "summer time": to compensate for this, simply add one hour to the times given.

THE CONSTELLATIONS OF THE SOUTHERN SKIES

These constellations are invisible from northern latitudes: Apus (the Bird of Paradise), Ara (the Altar), Carina (the Keel), Centaurus, Chamaeleon, Circinus (the Compasses), Crux (the Southern Cross), Dorado (the Swordfish), Horologium (the Clock), Hydrus (the Little Water Snake), Indus (the Indian), Lupus (the Wolf), Mensa (Table Mountain), Musca (the Fly), Octans (the Octant), Pavo (the Peacock), Phoenix, Pictor (the Painter's Easel), Reticulum (the Net), Telescopium, Triangulum Australe (the Southern Triangle), Tucana (the Toucan), Vela (the Sails), and Volans (the Flying Fish). Of course, you may well make a trip to the southern hemisphere, and you would want to take a look at the sky. So a very brief account is given here of the sights that are "not to be missed."

OBJECTS OF INTEREST IN THE SOUTHERN SKIES

The two Magellanic Clouds are considered the most remarkable features of the southern skies. They are seen as two light patches, slightly above the Galactic equator, and were noticed by the Portuguese navigator Ferdinand Magellan during his first circumnavigation of the globe. In fact they are two small, irregularly shaped galaxies which are satellites of the Milky Way. They are the only two galaxies in which individual stars can be distinguished with the naked eye, or even with binoculars. The Large Magellanic Cloud is in the constellation Dorado, and the Small Magellanic Cloud is in Tucana. Quite close to it, also in Tucana, is a very fine globular cluster that is easily seen with the naked eye: 47 Tucanae (also known as NGC 104). It is one of the closest to us, only 16,000 light years from the Sun. Another globular cluster which has been known for centuries can be seen in Centaurus: this is Omega Centauri. Also in Centaurus is the Solar System's nearest neighbor, Alpha Centauri. Another great curiosity is the star Beta Pictoris, near the Large Magellanic Cloud: in 1984 it was found to have a disk of dust around it, which must be a planetary system in course of formation. The disk cannot be seen with amateur instruments, but the magnitude 4 star is visible to the naked eye.

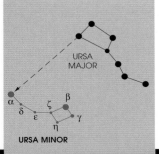

URSA MAJOR

URSA MINOR

The constellation of the Little Bear contains no galaxies or nebulae that can be seen with amateur equipment.

◁ Ursa Minor is not very easy to see with the naked eye. To find it, start with the two stars at the end of the Big Dipper in Ursa Major (the ones that form the side of the Dipper furthest from the handle), and extend the line that joins them until it reaches Polaris.

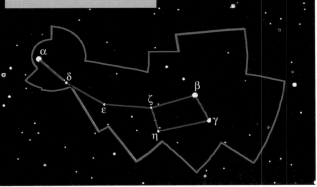

α (Alpha) URSAE MINORIS (POLARIS)

Mag 2.1 & 8.2

This is the brightest star in the constellation, and indicates the direction of celestial north: in fact, it is a little less than a degree away from true north. The periodic movement (precession) of Earth's axis in space will reduce this angular distance to less than half a degree by 2102. Polaris is a double star 460 light years from Earth. Its two components are only 18.3″ apart, and trying to resolve them is a good test of vision with a small telescope: the main difficulty lies in the great difference in brightness between the two bodies.

γ (Gamma) URSAE MINORIS (PHERKAD)

Mag 3.1

This is an irregular variable star, 270 light years distant. It changes by 0.1 magnitude (not enough to be noticeable to amateur observers) in the space of only two or three hours.

CEPHEUS

VISIBLE: all year

The constellation represents Cepheus, king of Ethiopia, husband of Cassiopeia, and father of Andromeda. It lies approximately between Ursa Minor and Cassiopeia.

Cepheus looks rather like a house. To find it, simply extend the line linking β (Beta) Ursae Majoris (Merak) and α (Alpha) Ursae Majoris (Dubhe) past Polaris, and you will come to γ (Gamma) Cephei. ▷

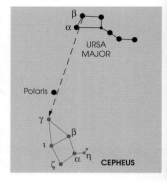

β (Beta) CEPHEI (ALFIRK)

Mag 3.2 & 7.9

This bright star has a companion star of magnitude 7.9, less than 14″ away, which can be resolved with a small telescope or binoculars. It was discovered in 1832. Alfirk is a variable star, with a short period (around 4½ hours) but only a slight variation in magnitude.

δ (Delta) CEPHEI

Mag 3.6 to 4.3

This star, 1,000 light years away, with a diameter 30 times as great as the Sun's, has given its name to a whole class of variable stars: the Cepheids. Its magnitude changes suddenly, in the course of half a day, from 3.6 to 4.3, and then falls again more slowly, over more than 4 days, making its period 5.3 days in all. In 1912, Henrietta Leavitt of Harvard discovered that there is a strict relationship between the period of variation of a Cepheid and its absolute luminosity; this makes it possible to compare the absolute magnitude of these stars with their observed relative magnitude, and thus to calculate the exact distance of each. Cepheids that have been found in nearby galaxies, such as the Magellanic Clouds and M33, have made it easy to calculate how far away these galaxies are.

KRÜGER 60

Mag 9.8 & 11.4

This double star can only be seen with a telescope. It is 13 light years away, making it one of our closest neighbors. The system consists of two red dwarfs only 9.2 AU apart, which is the same distance as between Saturn and the Sun. To the observer, these stars appear to touch, being separated by only 2.5″ of arc. Krüger 60B orbits Krüger 60A in just 44.5 years. The amateur wishing to observe Krüger 60 needs to be well equipped: a very

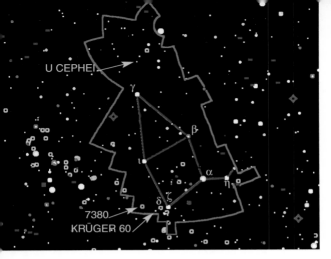

good star atlas is needed in order to find it, or astronomical software that is capable of showing faint stars in the area under observation. The minimum requirement for resolving the two bodies, and watching them revolve around one another over the course of a few years, is a 6-inch (150 mm) aperture telescope with a precision equatorial mount.

Coordinates: RA = 22h 26m 12s, Dec. = 57° 27′

ξ (Xi) CEPHEI

Mag
4.5 & 6.5

This star is in fact a physical binary system, the two components of which are only 7.7″ apart. The two stars are at a distance of around 120 light years from Earth.

U CEPHEI

Mag
6.8 to 9.2

The peculiar nature of this star was discovered in 1880: it is an eclipsing binary, which means that another, fainter star regularly passes in front of it, partly hiding it, so that its brightness then drops. U Cephei's companion eclipses it about every 2¹/₂ days, and over a period of 4 hours the brightness falls from 6.8 to 9.2. The eclipse lasts 2 hours. The two bodies are too close together to be resolved with a telescope. A good star atlas is needed for observing this system.

Coordinates: RA = 1h 2m, Dec. = 81° 51′ 30″

NGC 7380

Mag
7.2

This open cluster to the east of δ (Delta) Cephei is 11,700 light years away. It is made up of several dozen stars that can be made out with a small telescope.

DRACO

VISIBLE: all year

Draco, the Dragon, is a very large constellation that winds around Ursa Minor. Like Ursa Major, it never sets below the horizon for observers in mid-northern latitudes.

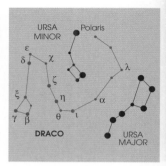

Draco stretches to the north of the Big Dipper's handle in Ursa Major. ▷

ψ (Psi) DRACONIS

Mag 4.9 & 6.1

This is a double star, 75 light years from Earth, which can be seen with binoculars and observed comfortably with a small telescope. Its two components are 30″ apart.

μ (Mu) DRACONIS

Mag 5.5 & 5.5

This is a system of two yellow stars some 100 light years away. They are of equal magnitude, and only separated by 2″ of arc. A 3-inch (75 mm) telescope is needed to resolve them.

NGC 6543

Mag 8.6

A planetary nebula of magnitude 8.6, located on a line between ζ (Zeta) and δ (Delta) Draconis, NGC 6543 can be observed with a small astronomical instrument, but looks very small: its apparent diameter is only 22″.

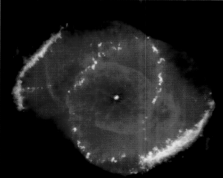

The planetary nebula NGC 6543 is a magnificent sight as seen by the Hubble Space Telescope. With amateur equipment, it appears as a very small object. ▷

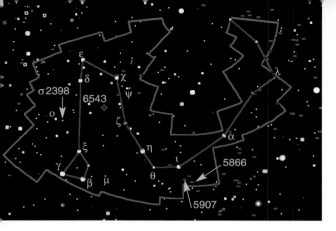

In fact, it looks like a star seen in a poorly focused telescope. The central star, with a magnitude of 9.6, should in theory be visible with a fairly small instrument, but in practice the nebulosity surrounding it makes it difficult to distinguish.

This nebula is at a distance of some 3,500 light years from Earth, and what appears to be just a "bubble of gas" is in reality about a third of a light year across.

Σ (Struve) 2398

Mag
8 & 8.5

This double star is visible with any telescope, but not to the naked eye, so it is not easy to find. It is located 1° west of the optical double o (Omicron) Draconis, and is one of the stars closest to our Solar System, since it is only about 11.5 light years away. But as it is composed of two small stars whose sizes are only 0.29 and 0.25 solar masses, the object appears quite faint, in spite of its proximity. The two components are separated by just over 15″ of arc, and the system bears a striking resemblance to 61 Cygni.

NGC 5866

Mag
10

This fuzzy and not very bright blob is in fact a giant elliptical galaxy, which we see from Earth precisely edge on. It lies roughly to the southwest of the star ι (Iota) Draconis, and to the west of NGC 5907 (another galaxy). This was once thought to be the object numbered 102 by Messier, but it is now known that Messier allocated this number in error, having in fact made a duplicate observation of M101, which is not far away. NGC 5866 cannot be seen easily with anything smaller than an 8-inch (200 mm) diameter telescope.

CASSIOPEIA

VISIBLE: all year

Cassiopeia was the queen of Cepheus, legendary king of Ethiopia. Her constellation is in the shape of a W, and in mid-northern latitudes can be seen throughout the year. This constellation is rich in variable stars and open clusters.

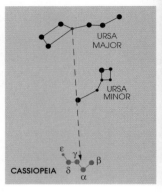

Cassiopeia is easy to find, on the far side of Polaris from Ursa Major. ▷

γ (Gamma) CASSIOPEIAE

Mag 1.6 to 3.3

This star is the centerpoint of Cassiopeia's W. It is an irregular variable, varying between magnitudes 1.6 and 3.3 without any fixed cycle. Until 1910 it had a constant magnitude of 2.25; after brightening to 1.6 in 1937, and fading to 3.3 in 1940, it seemed to have stabilized at around 2.2 in the mid-1970s. Nobody can predict how it will vary in future. γ (Gamma) Cassiopeiae has a companion star of magnitude 11, 2″ away, which is very difficult to see.

ι (Iota) CASSIOPEIAE

Mag 4 & 7

This physical three-star system is one of the most remarkable examples of its type. With a 3-inch (75 mm) telescope it is possible to distinguish a yellow primary star with two blue companions at angular distances of 2.3″ and 7.2″. The group is about 180 light years from Earth.

R CASSIOPEIAE

Mag 4.8 to 13.6

This star, a long-period variable red giant of the Mira type, is at times so faint that it can seem to have disappeared. Over 431 days it goes from magnitude 4.8 (visible with the naked eye) to 13.6 (only visible with a telescope of 8 inches (200 mm) or more). R Cassiopeiae is approximately 800 light years away.

M103

Mag 7

Cassiopeia is on the Galactic equator, so it is not at all surprising that it contains a number of open clusters. M103 is one of the easiest to observe

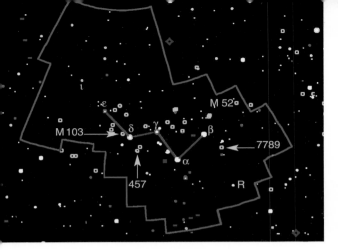

of all its clusters. It is easy to find, located 1° northeast of δ (Delta) Cassiopeiae, and has an apparent overall magnitude of 7. It is 8,000 light years from Earth, and seems to belong to the same group of open clusters as NGC 654 and NGC 659, which are approximately the same distance away.

M52

Mag 6.9

Exactly in line with the stars α (Alpha) and β (Beta) Cassiopeiae, M52 is one of the finest open clusters in the constellation. Charles Messier discovered it in 1774 while observing a comet. It contains around 200 stars in an area 15 light years across; in fact, it is among the densest open clusters known.

NGC 457

Mag 6.4

This is another open cluster which makes a fine sight in an amateur's telescope. It contains around a hundred giant stars which seem to be quite young. It is 9,300 light years away, and appears to be less than 30 light years across.

NGC 7789

Mag 6.7

This open cluster is one of the richest we know, containing at least a thousand stars. With binoculars, it appears as just a small, indistinct blob: it takes a small telescope to reveal that it is in fact made up of very closely packed stars. It is 6,000 light years distant and measures 50 light years across.

Visible: all year

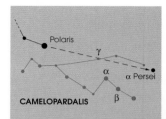

Polaris
γ
α
α Persei
β

CAMELOPARDALIS

Next door to Cassiopeia, Camelopardalis (the Giraffe) remains visible at all times of the year. It has no particularly bright stars.

◁ *To find Camelopardalis, follow the line of the last two stars in the tail of Ursa Minor, itself not very easy to make out.*

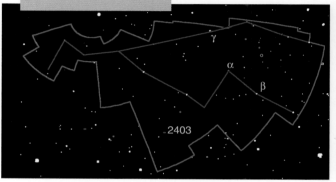

γ
α
β
2403

NGC 2403

Mag
8

This galaxy, 11 million light years away, can be made out with binoculars in good conditions (when the sky is really dark), and it is easy to see with a telescope. It is one of the closest neighbors to the Local Group of galaxies that contains the Milky Way, and probably belongs to the same group as M81 and M82 in Ursa Major. From its apparent diameter of 16′ astronomers estimate that it is actually 37,000 light years across. Long-exposure photographs from the largest observatories show a great cloud of hydrogen, 880 light years in diameter, centered on the galaxy's nucleus. The shape of NGC 2403 is similar to that of M33.

◁ *The spiral galaxy NGC 2403 is one of the easiest for amateurs to observe.*

VISIBLE: summer (on Meridian at 21:00 in early August)

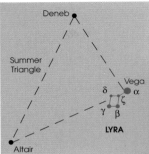

This small constellation in the shape of a parallelogram represents the musical instrument associated with Orpheus.

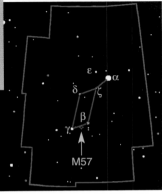

M57

△ *Lyra is not hard to find, since its principal star, Vega, is the fifth brightest in the sky and forms one of the points of the Summer Triangle.*

ε (Epsilon) LYRAE

Mag
5 & 5

Located next to Vega and easy to find, this star was recognized by the astronomer William Herschel in 1779 as a double-double star: though it looks like a double star, each of its components is in fact itself double (though separated by only 3″). A 3-inch (75 mm) telescope is needed to resolve this four-star system, which is 120 light years away.

M57

Mag
9

M57 is one of the easiest of the planetary nebulae to find and observe. It lies exactly between β (Beta) and γ (Gamma) Lyrae, and can be seen with a small telescope as a tiny ring. At the center of the nebula is a star of magnitude 14.7, which can only be made out with a 14-inch (350 mm) telescope: this is a white dwarf nearing the end of its life. The sphere expanding and dispersing around it is gas which it has emitted. In around 5,000 million years our own Sun will end in the same way.

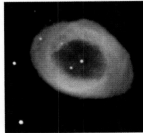

In this picture, taken with a large telescope, two stars can be seen inside the gaseous ring. Only the one at the ring's exact center is associated with M57. ▷

URSA MAJOR

all year

Ursa Major, the Great Bear, can be seen from the northern hemisphere at all times of year and is easy to recognize: its principal stars trace the outline of a big ladle or "dipper," also known as the Plough.

It is very easy to find Ursa Major: simply look up to the north, in the general direction of Polaris. ▷

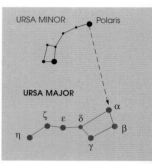

ζ (Zeta) URSAE MAJORIS (MIZAR)

Mag 2.5 & 4

This star, 88 light years away, is in fact accompanied by several others, forming a multiple star system. Observers with good eyesight will be able to make out, just beside the principal star (11′ 50″ away), another star of magnitude 4, which is known as Alcor. Apparently there is no gravitational connection between them, and they are 15 light years apart. Mizar itself has a magnitude 4 companion, 14.5″ of arc away.

M101

Mag 7

To find M101, start from ζ (Zeta) Ursae Majoris (Mizar) and simply look along the approximate line formed by four magnitude 4 and 5 stars to the east of it. This object, cataloged by Messier, is a spiral galaxy which we see "from above." Its spiral arms, however, can only be seen with large telescopes or in long photographic exposures. The galaxy is around 20 million light years away and is 90,000 light years across, with a total mass equal to that of 16,000 million Suns. Three supernovae have been observed there since 1909.

◁ *M101 is a magnificent spiral galaxy, and one of the closest to the Milky Way.*

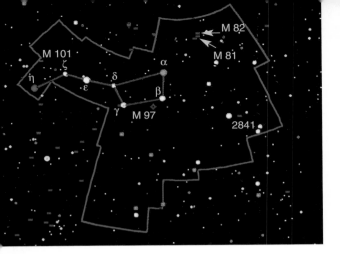

M81

In the northern part of the constellation is M81, one of the easiest galaxies to observe with a small telescope. It looks like an oval blob; although it is a spiral galaxy, the spiral arms are not easy to make out. It is only 9 million light years away, and belongs to the closest group of galaxies in our Local Cluster. M81 has as a close neighbor another fairly bright galaxy, M82.

M82

Mag 8

Just next door to M81 is M82, which is 20 million light years from Earth. Seen in a telescope, it looks like a spiral galaxy viewed edge on, but in fact it is an irregular shape. With a 10-inch (250 mm) aperture instrument, some dark structures can be made out, which partially obscure the galaxy's nucleus.

NGC 2841

Mag 9

Close to θ (Theta) Ursae Majoris, NGC 2841 is a similar galaxy to M81, but much less bright and therefore harder to see.

M97

Mag 11

This is a planetary nebula, probably one of the closest and largest we know. It lies at a distance of 1,300 light years, and is 3 light years across. With a telescope 4 inches (100 mm) or more in diameter, it appears as a quite extensive, fuzzy patch, very pale against the dark background of the night sky.

CANES VENATICI

Vɪsɪʙʟᴇ: summer (on Meridian at 21:00 in early June)

This constellation, the Hunting Dogs, was given its name by Johannes Hevelius in the seventeenth century. It is of medium size and contains a number of Messier's objects, including one of the loveliest spiral galaxies in the sky.

It is very easy to locate the Canes Venatici, just below (to the south of) the handle of the Big Dipper in Ursa Major. ▷

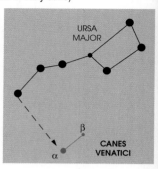

α (Alpha) CANUM VENATICORUM (COR CAROLI)

Mag 3 & 5.5

This, the brightest star in the constellation, was named by Edmond Halley "the Heart of Charles" in honor of King Charles I. It is of interest to observers because it is a binary that is easy to find and to study with a small telescope. Although since 1830 no movement has been detected between the two components, which are separated by 20″ of arc, this is certainly a true, physical binary, 110 light years from the Solar System. The principal star varies in brightness over a period of 5½ days, but it only changes by 0.05 magnitude, which is not enough for an amateur astronomer to detect.

M51

Mag 8

This is a spiral galaxy which we view "from above," and one of the most spectacular in the whole sky. To the south of η (Eta) Ursae Majoris

(Benetnash), it was discovered by Messier in October 1773. It shines with a magnitude of 8, which makes it easy for amateurs to observe. In a small telescope, however, only two faint and indistinct blobs can be seen, looking like two distant globular clusters side by side. The larger of these is in fact the galaxy's nucleus, while the other is a small, irregularly shaped galaxy inter-acting with the first. A telescope

◁ *The Whirlpool Galaxy is one of the finest sights in the night sky.*

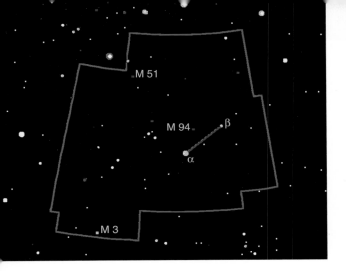

5 to 6 inches (125 to 150 mm) in diameter is needed in order to detect the prominent spiral arms around the nucleus, which gave it the name of Whirlpool Galaxy. This formation was first noticed in 1850, by the Irish peer Lord Rosse, using a giant refracting telescope 72 inches (1.8 m) in diameter. Nowadays, a 12-inch (300 mm) telescope of amateur standard is all it takes to give a clear image of the spiral arms. M51 is 28 million light years away, and its mass is 160,000 million solar masses. It measures some 100,000 light years across.

M3

Mag 6.4

Right next to the southern boundary of the constellation, M3 is one of the finest globular clusters in the sky. Though it cannot be seen with the naked eye, the weakest pair of binoculars will bring it leaping into view. A telescope of over 6 inches (150 mm) reveals hundreds of stars, a truly magical sight. Over 45,000 stars have been counted in this cluster, which is 220 light years across and 32,000 light years away. They include a number of Cepheid variables.

M94

Mag 8

This beautiful spiral galaxy, shaped like an almost perfect circle, lies to the east of β (Beta) Canum Venaticorum. It has a brilliant nucleus 30″ in diameter, which gives it a spherical appearance in a telescope, but long-exposure photographs taken with powerful instruments have revealed its system of spiral arms, which are much less bright. The galaxy is 33,000 light years across and 16 million light years away.

CYGNUS

This constellation lies exactly on the Galactic equator, and can be recognized by its X shape. Deneb is its brightest star, and with Vega and Altair it makes up the Summer Triangle.

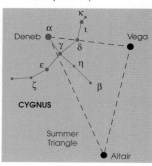

Cygnus is easy to find with the help of Deneb, which belongs to the Summer Triangle. ▷

χ (Chi) CYGNI

Mag 3.6 to 14.2

This is a variable star with a long period and a great variation in magnitude. It takes 407 days to go from its brightest (visible to the naked eye) to its faintest (only visible with a 10-inch (250 mm) telescope or larger).

61 CYGNI

Mag 5.2 & 6

This splendid double star is one of the Solar System's closest neighbors, only 11 light years away. It consists of two yellow stars very similar to the Sun, and of almost equal brightness. A small telescope with an aperture of no more than 2½ inches (60 mm) will give a good view of this physical binary, whose components are now 30″ apart. However, the angular distance alters over a 653-year period, the time taken by 61 Cygni B to orbit 61 Cygni A. In 1650 the angle was only 11″, and it will reach a maximum of 34″ in the year 2100 before starting to decrease again.

NGC 7000 (NORTH AMERICA NEBULA)

Mag 16

This is one of the best known objects in the sky, though it is not easy to observe. It is a large nebula, 3,600 light years away, with an extraordinary

shape that resembles the continent of North America. However, it is very spread

◁ *The elusive North America Nebula requires a 4-inch (100 mm) telescope with a wide-angle eyepiece. The nebula to the right in this photograph is the Pelican Nebula.*

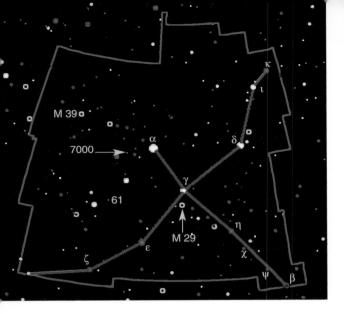

out (extending over 1.5° of arc) and not very bright. Because of its poor definition, you are mostly likely to detect it with the help of a telescope with a short focal length, which gives low magnification but a broad field of view. It should then be possible to pick out the region known as the Gulf of Mexico.

M29

6.6

This group of stars with individual magnitudes of 8 or 9 is an open cluster with an overall magnitude of 6.6, about 5,400 light years away. With a telescope, the brightest stars can be seen to form a trapezoid pattern. The cluster is in the region of 10 light years across.

M39

Mag 4.6

This is an open cluster, so extensive that an ordinary astronomical telescope cannot view all of its stars at once. Amateur astronomers are therefore better off observing M39 with binoculars, in which it looks quite spectacular. It is in fact only 7 light years across, and its great apparent size is due to its relative proximity to Earth (880 light years). The stars that make up this cluster appear to be scarcely older than the young stars in the Pleiades.

ANDROMEDA

VISIBLE: fall (on Meridian at 21:00 in early November)

Andromeda was the daughter of Cepheus, legendary king of Ethiopia. Her constellation is best known for containing the Andromeda Galaxy; its stars are not particularly bright.

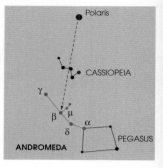

Andromeda is fairly easy to find, to the south of the W in Cassiopeia. One of its stars also forms a corner of the Great Square of Pegasus. ▷

γ (Gamma) ANDROMEDAE (ALMACH)

Mag 2.3 & 5.1

This bright star with its orange color is easy to locate with the naked eye. It is 355 light years away. Almach is the principal component of a three-star system, but this is very difficult to see, even with a telescope. The bluish star which orbits Almach in a period of 61 years is never more than 10″ away, and it in turn has a companion, of magnitude 6.6, at an angular distance of just 0.5″.

π (Pi) ANDROMEDAE

Mag 4.5 & 9

This is a double star 470 light years from Earth. It is a favorite object for amateurs with a small telescope, such as a 2½-inch (60 mm) refractor, because the angular distance of 36″ between the components makes them easy to resolve.

R ANDROMEDAE

Mag 5.3 & 15.1

This is a variable star which seems to disappear every now and then. Its brightness varies over a period of 409 days from magnitude 5.3 (visible with the naked eye) to 15.1 (invisible even with the aid of an 8-inch (200 mm) telescope).

M31

Mag 3

M31 is a spiral galaxy, and one of the most spectacular objects in the whole vault of the sky. It can be seen as an oval blob by the naked eye, and is included in a Persian map of the heavens dating from A.D. 964. First observed with a telescope in the seventeenth century, it was known as the Andromeda "Nebula" until 1929, when the American astronomer Edwin Hubble discovered that it was in fact a galaxy. Apart from the two

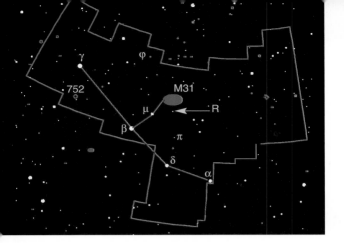

Magellanic Clouds and some other small satellite galaxies of the Milky Way, M31 is the galaxy closest to our own, at a distance of only 2.5 million light years. It is as much as 110,000 light years across and has a mass twice that of the Milky Way, containing some 400,000 million solar masses. With binoculars or a basic telescope, only the central part of M31 (its nucleus) can be seen: the spiral arms are only visible with very large telescopes or in long-exposure photographs. But even the smaller instruments reveal its great size: it extends over more than 2° of arc (four times the apparent diameter of the Moon). There are also two small elliptical galaxies, satellites of M31, which can only be seen with a telescope: M32 and NGC 205.

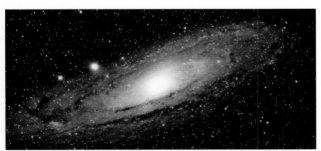

△ M31 is the closest spiral galaxy to the Milky Way. It is easy to see, but the spiral arms can only be made out with a large telescope.

NGC 752

Mag 5.7

Astronomers have counted 60 stars in this open cluster, which is 1,300 light years distant.

PERSEUS

VISIBLE: winter (on Meridian at 21:00 in early January)

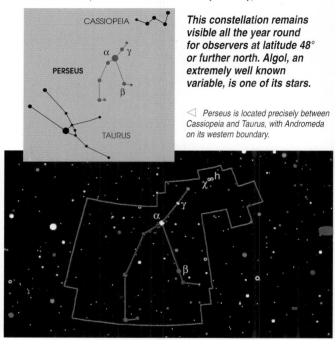

This constellation remains visible all the year round for observers at latitude 48° or further north. Algol, an extremely well known variable, is one of its stars.

◁ *Perseus is located precisely between Cassiopeia and Taurus, with Andromeda on its western boundary.*

β (Beta) PERSEI (ALGOL)

Mag 2.1 to 3.4

This brilliant star is in fact a binary, 93 light years away, whose components are 3.2 and 3.4 times the diameter of the Sun. They are too close together to be seen separately. They orbit each other in less than three days. Every 2 days, 20 hours, and 48 minutes, the fainter star almost totally eclipses its brighter companion, causing a dramatic drop in luminosity which lasts for 10 hours. This kind of system is known as an eclipsing binary.

NGC 869 & 884 (DOUBLE CLUSTER)

Mag 4.4 & 4.3

The two indistinct blobs which constitute the Double Cluster, h Persei and χ (Chi) Persei, can be seen with the naked eye. They are respectively 7,200 and 7,500 light years away, and each contains more than 300 stars.

Visible: fall (on Meridian at 21:00 in early October)

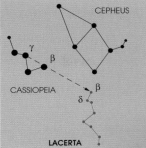

Lacerta, or the Lizard, is tucked in between Cygnus and Andromeda. The constellation only dates from 1690, when Johannes Hevelius gave it this name. Its stars are relatively faint, so it is not easy to recognize.

△ *Lacerta occupies a region of the sky rather poor in bright stars, surrounded by Cassiopeia, Cepheus, Cygnus, the Great Square of Pegasus, and Andromeda. β (Beta) Lacertae can be found by extending the line joining γ (Gamma) Cassiopeiae to β (Beta) Cassiopeiae.*

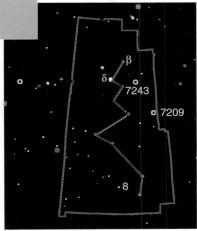

NGC 7243

Mag 6.4

This is an open cluster with an overall magnitude of 6.4, extending over an area 20′ across. It is 2,900 light years away and contains 40 stars.

8 LACERTAE

Mag 6 & 6.6

In addition to the two principal components (one of which is at the limit of visibility with the naked eye), this multiple system contains two other stars, of magnitudes 10.5 and 9.5.

NGC 7209

Mag 6.7

Another open cluster, like NGC 7243 2,900 light years away, but with the slightly larger apparent diameter of 25′. It contains around 25 stars, with magnitudes between 9 and 12.

LYNX

Visible: spring (on Meridian at 21:00 in early March)

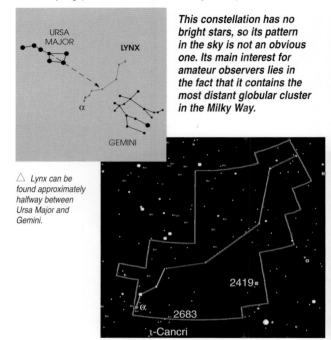

This constellation has no bright stars, so its pattern in the sky is not an obvious one. Its main interest for amateur observers lies in the fact that it contains the most distant globular cluster in the Milky Way.

△ *Lynx can be found approximately halfway between Ursa Major and Gemini.*

NGC 2683

Mag 9

This edge-on spiral galaxy is not easy to locate, although it can be found by looking 4° 32′ to the north of ι (Iota) Cancri. It is easily seen in a 4-inch (100 mm) telescope.

NGC 2419

Mag 10.4

This globular cluster, discovered by William Herschel as a "nebula" in 1788, has been nicknamed the Intergalactic Wanderer, because it is so far from the center of the Milky Way. At 300,000 light years from the Sun, it is one of the most distant globular clusters surrounding the Galaxy. It is at such a distance (further from our Solar System than the Magellanic Clouds) that its apparent diameter of 4.1′, visible only in photographs, makes it actually 300 light years across.

VISIBLE: spring (on Meridian at 21:00 in mid-April)

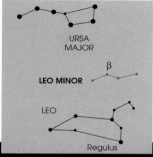

Leo Minor, the Little Lion, is without doubt the poorest constellation of them all.

◁ To find Leo Minor, first identify Regulus, the brightest star in the constellation Leo. Then look north: Leo Minor lies between Leo and Ursa Major.

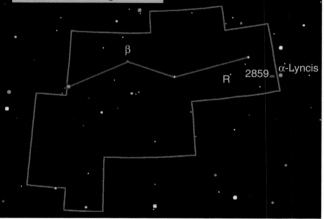

NGC 2859

Mag 10

Leo Minor contains only faint galaxies. NGC 2859, which is a spiral galaxy, is the least difficult to find, since it lies just 40′ east of the brightest star in the neighboring constellation Lynx. This is α (Alpha) Lyncis, of magnitude 3.3.
Coordinates: RA = 9h 24.3m, Dec. = 34° 31′ 5″

R LEONIS MINORIS

Mag 6.3 to 13

This is a variable star of the Mira type, with a period of just over a year (372 days). Although, even when at its brightest, R Leonis Minoris is barely visible with the naked eye, it can be observed with a very small pair of binoculars.

COMA BERENICES

Visible: spring (on Meridian at 21:00 in mid-May)

*Several stars can be seen with
the naked eye in the well
known Coma open cluster.
With a telescope, a number of
globular clusters and galaxies
can be observed.*

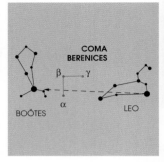

*Coma Berenices is bordered by Leo to the
west, Boötes to the east, Canes Venatici
to the north and Virgo to the south. It is
not hard to find, as it lies on a line
between Regulus and Arcturus.* ▷

COMA STAR CLUSTER

Mag
ind

This open cluster is not included either in Messier's list or in the *New
General Catalogue* (NGC), and it is true that, with its apparent diameter
of 5° (ten times that of the Moon), it looks more like a particularly starry
region of the sky than an object in its own right. The ideal way to observe
it is with a pair of binoculars, because they have a wide enough field to
show all its stars at once. This group of stars is about 250 light years from
the Solar System.

35 COMAE BERENICES

Mag
5, 7.5 & 9

This star is in fact a triple system, but you will need a clear sky and a
telescope at least 5 inches (125 mm) in diameter to have any chance of
resolving two of the components. Their magnitudes are 5 and 7.5, and
they are only 1.2″ apart, revolving around one another in 675 years. The
third component, of magnitude 9, can be resolved with any instrument,
since it is 29″ distant from the other two.

M53

Mag
7.7

This globular cluster, 56,000 light years distant, is an easy target for small
telescopes, although one of at least 6 inches (150 mm) will be needed to
resolve any of its individual stars. The cluster lies 1° northeast of α (Alpha)
Comae Berenices (Diadem). Just 1° to the southeast there is another,
much fainter, globular cluster: NGC 5053.

NGC 5053

Mag
9.8

Though less bright than M53, NGC 5053 is in fact closer: 50,000 light
years from Earth, compared with 56,000. Because of its loose structure,
this object was once classified as an extremely rich open cluster. It is,

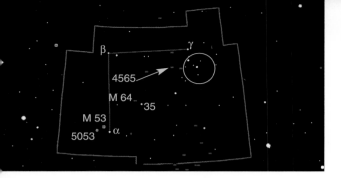

however, a globular cluster, distant not only from Earth, but also from the Galactic equator.

M64 (BLACK EYE GALAXY)

Mag 8

Quite close to the triple star 35 Comae Berenices (1° east-northeast of it) is the galaxy known as the Black Eye Galaxy because of a dark structure, believed to be dust, surrounding its nucleus. This is a spiral galaxy, seen by us almost full on. The dark band around it cannot be distinguished clearly with anything less than a 6-inch (150 mm) telescope: anyone using a smaller instrument would require very good eyesight and excellent viewing conditions. The Black Eye Galaxy is 36,000 light years across and 19 million light years distant.

NGC 4565

Mag 9

This is the only galaxy in the Virgo Galaxy Cluster to be treated here. It is the best known example of a spiral galaxy seen exactly edge on, and also the largest. Even with a telescope as small as 5 inches (125 mm) in diameter, its long, thin shape can be detected, but a 10-inch (250 mm) instrument is needed in order to make out the dark band of interstellar

dust which forms a stripe along its entire length. This galaxy is about 20 million light years away and 90,000 light years across.

◁ *The best known of spiral galaxies seen edge on is NGC 4565. It shows how the Milky Way would look if viewed from outside at the same angle.*

AURIGA

Visible: winter (on Meridian at 21:00 in early February)

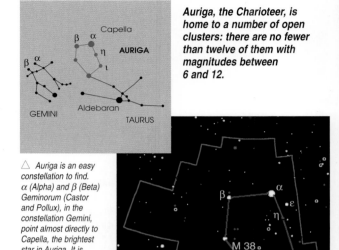

Auriga, the Charioteer, is home to a number of open clusters: there are no fewer than twelve of them with magnitudes between 6 and 12.

△ *Auriga is an easy constellation to find. α (Alpha) and β (Beta) Geminorum (Castor and Pollux), in the constellation Gemini, point almost directly to Capella, the brightest star in Auriga. It is located northeast of Taurus and its prominent red star, Aldebaran.*

M36

Mag 6

This is one of a group of three open clusters in Auriga that are extremely easy to observe. It has some 60 stars, of magnitudes 9 to 14. These are young stars, 4,100 light years away.

M37

Mag 5.6

This cluster of 150 stars is the brightest of the three, and most impressive when seen in an ordinary telescope. It is around 4,400 light years away.

M38

Mag 6.4

This third cluster has around a hundred stars. It is 4,300 light years distant, and its apparent diameter of 20′ means that it is in fact 25 light years across.

BOÖTES

Visible: spring (on Meridian at 22:00 in mid-June)

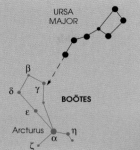

Boötes, guardian of the nearby Great Bear (Ursa Major), is quite an extensive constellation. It contains some interesting double stars which provide a good test of vision, but little else of note.

△ *Continue the line of the Big Dipper's handle to find the middle of Boötes. α (Alpha) Boötis (Arcturus) is a prominent star of magnitude –0.1, and this landmark makes Boötes an easy constellation to find.*

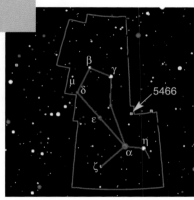

ε (Epsilon) BOÖTIS (IZAR)

Mag 2.5 & 5

This is a fine double star which can be seen with a small astronomical instrument of 2½ inches (50 mm) by anyone with a little experience. The larger component shines bright orange, while its companion emits mainly blue light. The system is 210 light years from Earth.

μ (Mu) BOÖTIS (ALKALUROPS)

Mag 4.5, 6.5 & 7

Alkalurops is in fact a triple star. There are two objects 108″ apart, and the fainter one is a physical binary consisting of two stars similar to the Sun. These are just 2″ apart and take about 246 years to orbit one another.

NGC 5466

Mag 9.1

This globular cluster, 70,000 light years away, can be observed to the north of Arcturus.

CORONA BOREALIS

Visible: summer (on Meridian at 21:00 in early July)

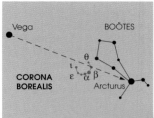

This little constellation contains no galaxies visible to amateurs, no star clusters, and no nebulae. Its interest lies in its variable stars, which include one recurrent nova.

△ *Corona Borealis has an easily recognized crescent shape, and can be found without much difficulty on a line between Vega (in Lyra) and Arcturus (in Boötes). The handle of the Big Dipper also points roughly in its direction.*

ζ (Zeta) CORONAE BOREALIS

Mag 5 & 6

This double star makes a relatively easy object for amateurs equipped with only a small telescope, because its two components are at a distance of 6.3″.

T CORONAE BOREALIS

Mag 2 or 3 to 10

For most of the time, this is a faint (magnitude 10) and uninteresting star. It lies to the southeast of ε (Epsilon) Coronae Borealis, but is not easy to find if you have a small instrument. However, it is a recurrent nova which has already flared up spectacularly, once in 1866 and again in 1946. On those occasions, for periods of a few days, it attained magnitudes of 2 and 3 respectively.

R CORONAE BOREALIS

Mag 5.6 to 14.8

Visible to the naked eye for most of the time, this irregular variable can disappear when its magnitude drops to nearly 15.

Visible: summer (on Meridian at 21:00 in mid-September)

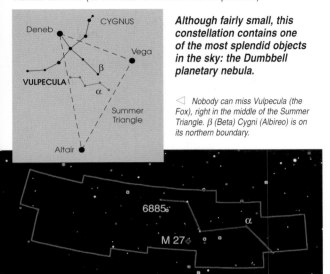

Although fairly small, this constellation contains one of the most splendid objects in the sky: the Dumbbell planetary nebula.

◁ *Nobody can miss Vulpecula (the Fox), right in the middle of the Summer Triangle. β (Beta) Cygni (Albireo) is on its northern boundary.*

M27 (DUMBBELL NEBULA)

Mag 8

A small telescope or a pair of 3¹/₂-inch (80 mm) binoculars will reveal one of the most beautiful planetary nebulae in the whole sky. This is an

expanding gaseous sphere surrounding a star of magnitude 13.4. Since it is 900 light years distant, its apparent angular dimensions (8′ × 5′) make it actually 2.5 light years across. With a 6-inch (150 mm) telescope, it is possible to appreciate the nebula's unusual symmetrical shape.

◁ *The Dumbbell planetary nebula is a graphic illustration of how our own Sun will end.*

NGC 6885

 Mag 5.7

4° 30′ northeast of the Dumbbell is an open cluster that can be seen with the naked eye: NGC 6885. It has 30 stars of magnitudes 6 to 12, in an area 7′ across.

HERCULES

This summer constellation contains some interesting double stars, but its main attraction is the well known globular cluster M13, the brightest in the northern sky.

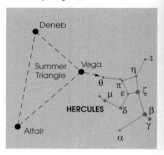

The constellation Hercules is next door to Lyra, so it is easy to find from the bright star Vega. ▷

α (Alpha) HERCULIS (RASALGETHI)

Mag 2.7 to 4

This star, 380 light years away, is a red giant with a diameter four hundred times that of the Sun. It is a variable star with an average period of 90 days, during which its magnitude changes from 4.0 to 2.7 and back. It is also a very fine double star for amateur astronomers to observe: the companion, of magnitude 5.4, is 4.6″ away, and the two stars form an orange/emerald pair.

δ (Delta) HERCULIS

Mag 3 & 8.5

This double star is an optical double, meaning that its components have no gravitational connection with each other: the two stars are in fact at a great distance from each other, and each has its own proper motion. They are moving "past" each other: their angular distance decreased to a minimum of 9″ in 1960 and has been growing since then. It is around 10″ at present.

ζ (Zeta) HERCULIS

Mag 2.9 & 5.5

Easily identified with the naked eye, this star 35 light years away is in fact a double, but a telescope is needed to resolve its two components, which are only 1″ apart on average. The fainter star orbits the other in a little over 34 years, making this one of the few double stars one may see through a complete revolution in the course of a lifetime.

μ (Mu) HERCULIS

Mag 3.5, 9.5 & 10

This is in fact a triple system. Two of its components are very easy to see, since they are 34″ apart. But the fainter of these two stars itself has a companion, which is only 1.3″ away and orbits it with a period of 43 years.

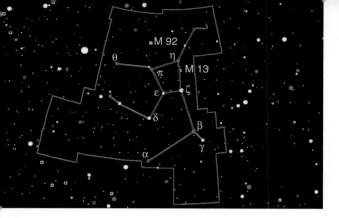

This triple system is relatively close to Earth, since it is only 27 light years distant.

M13 (GREAT CLUSTER)

Mag 5.9

Since its magnitude is 5.9, the globular cluster M13 is theoretically visible to the naked eye. In practice, it is not, but it does make a splendid sight in binoculars. It lies 2° 20′ of arc from η (Eta) Herculis in the direction of ζ (Zeta) Herculis, and looks like a whitish gaseous sphere. In a 4-inch (100 mm) telescope it appears as a fairly extensive cloud (the apparent diameter is 17′), and with a 6-inch (150 mm) instrument individual stars can be made out within the cluster. A telescope with a diameter of 8 inches (200 mm) or more makes it a magical sight, and with still larger instruments it is possible to detect a dark, Y-shaped feature apparently on the luminous surface of the cluster. This was first noticed by the Irish observer Bindon Stoney in the nineteenth century. The "mark" would seem to be due to interstellar dust absorbing the stars' light. The cluster, which is a sphere 200 light years across, contains at least 300,000 stars and is 23,500 light years away.

◁ *M13, the brightest globular cluster in the northern sky, is an easy and rewarding object for beginners to observe.*

M92

Mag 6.5

This is another globular cluster, not so bright as M13 but still one of the finest objects of its kind for observation. It is at a distance of 25,500 light years from Earth.

SAGITTA

VISIBLE: summer (on Meridian at 21:00 in early September)

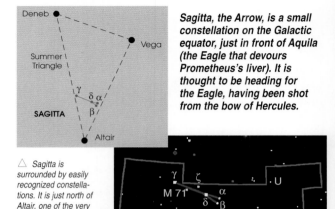

Sagitta, the Arrow, is a small constellation on the Galactic equator, just in front of Aquila (the Eagle that devours Prometheus's liver). It is thought to be heading for the Eagle, having been shot from the bow of Hercules.

△ *Sagitta is surrounded by easily recognized constellations. It is just north of Altair, one of the very bright stars that form the Summer Triangle.*

ε (Epsilon) SAGITTAE

Mag 5.5 & 7.5

Just below α (Alpha) Sagittae (Sham), the principal star in the constellation, this is one of the easiest double stars to resolve. The two components are 88″ apart, and even with binoculars they can be seen as two distinct bodies. They are 325 light years from Earth.

U SAGITTAE

Mag 6.4 to 9

Like β (Beta) Persei (Algol), this is an eclipsing binary. But while Algol is only partially eclipsed by its companion, the smaller member of U Sagittae is entirely hidden every 3 days, 9 hours, and 8 minutes by the larger, but fainter star. For an hour and 40 minutes it shines with only one-tenth of its usual brightness, falling from magnitude 6.5 to 9.2. It easy to follow the variation by comparing it with the nearby star S 2504, which is normally slightly fainter. U Sagittae is 1.7° west of a small group of stars that belongs to the neighboring constellation Vulpecula.
Coordinates: RA = 19h 16m 6s, Dec. = 19° 31′

M71

Mag 8

Astronomers are now agreed that M71 should be classed as a globular cluster, rather than as an open cluster. It is a magnitude 8 object that can be observed by amateurs, and is 13,000 light years away and over 20 light years across.

VISIBLE: summer (on Meridian at 21:00 in mid-September)

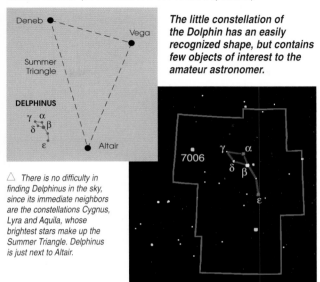

The little constellation of the Dolphin has an easily recognized shape, but contains few objects of interest to the amateur astronomer.

△ *There is no difficulty in finding Delphinus in the sky, since its immediate neighbors are the constellations Cygnus, Lyra and Aquila, whose brightest stars make up the Summer Triangle. Delphinus is just next to Altair.*

γ (Gamma) DELPHINI

Mag
4.5 & 5.5

This star, a physical binary, was discovered to be double in 1830 and is an ideal object for amateurs with small telescopes. One of its components appears yellow and the other slightly greenish. They are 10″ apart, and parallax measurement shows that this binary system is a little over 100 light years away.

NGC 7006

Mag
10

This is one of the most difficult globular clusters to observe. This is not surprising, for it is among the more distant of these objects. It lies 150,000 light years from the center of the Milky Way and 115,000 light years from the Solar System. This means that it is virtually outside the Galaxy, for the Magellanic Clouds, two of the Milky Way's satellite galaxies, are only a little further away. A 6-inch (150 mm) telescope is needed for any chance of seeing NGC 7006 as even a small, pale blob, without resolving any individual stars.

TAURUS

Taurus, the Bull, is one of the constellations of the Zodiac, and holds great interest for the amateur observer. Two spectacular open clusters can be seen with the naked eye: the Pleiades and the Hyades.

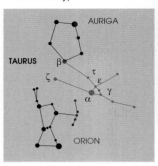

Taurus's very brilliant principal star, Aldebaran, makes it fairly easy to find, and its pattern is clearly outlined by a number of bright stars. It lies northwest of Orion and south of Auriga. ▷

α (Alpha) TAURI (ALDEBARAN)

Mag 0.9 & 13

The brightest star in Taurus is also the fourteenth brightest in the whole sky. The name Aldebaran means "the follower" (of the Pleiades). It is a red giant, 65 light years away, and about 40 times the diameter of the Sun. It has a companion at an angular distance of 31.4″, a magnitude 13 red dwarf which is very hard to see: since they have the same proper motion, they probably form a physical binary. There is also an optical companion, a star of magnitude 11 at a distance of 121″, which is easier to detect.

σ (Sigma) TAURI

Mag 4.8 & 5.1

This is a double star visible to the naked eye, quite close to α (Alpha) Tauri (Aldebaran). Its components are 431″ of arc apart.

τ (Tau) TAURI

Mag 4 & 8

This star, 7° north of Aldebaran, can be seen with the naked eye. It is in fact a physical binary, but binoculars are needed to see the two components separately. They are 63″ apart and 490 light years from Earth.

THE HYADES

Mag ind

The open cluster known as the Hyades extends over more than 4°, and its V-shaped pattern forms the head of the Bull. Aldebaran nearby appears to belong to it but is in fact much nearer to the Solar System: the center of the Hyades is some 150 light years away. This central area, extending over 3.5°, is 8 light years across and contains a number of fainter stars which can only be made out with a telescope. In all, the cluster contains at least 250 stars, most with magnitudes between 12 and 16. The Hyades is best observed with a pair of binoculars.

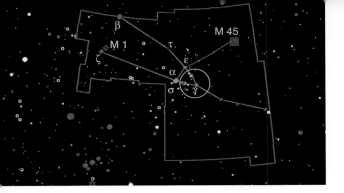

M45 (THE PLEIADES)

Mag 1.2

This fine cluster looks to the naked eye like a group of six or seven stars; under good viewing conditions, some observers are able to make out as many as eleven. For a really good view of the cluster, a pair of 7×50 binoculars is ideal, giving a large enough field of view to show all the major stars at once. The Pleiades are large, young stars over 400 light years away, still surrounded by nebulosity which can generally be seen only in long-exposure photographs. However, a few observers have succeeded in discerning the veil surrounding Merope with the aid of an 8-inch (200 mm) telescope.

Alcyone, Maia, Taygete, Electra, Merope, and Atlas, the major stars of the Pleiades, surrounded by nebulosity. ▷

M1 (CRAB NEBULA)

Mag 8

This object, the very first to be listed by Charles Messier, is a supernova remnant: all that remains of a star that exploded in July 1054. The event was noticed by Chinese astronomers and by the Navajo in America. After the explosion, the star became a pulsar of magnitude 15.9 (quite invisible to amateurs), with a surrounding envelope that constitutes the nebula M1. It is 6,300 light years away and consists of a constantly expanding cloud

of gas, visible in a small telescope as a very pale blob a little over 1° north of ζ (Zeta) Tauri. Even with an 8-inch (200 mm) telescope, all that can be seen is an indistinct cloud.

◁ *The Crab Nebula is the remnant of a supernova that exploded in 1054.*

GEMINI

VISIBLE: winter (on Meridian at 21:00 in mid-February)

The constellation of the Twins, part of the Zodiac, is worth studying for its remarkable open clusters and for one of the strangest of all planetary nebulae, NGC 2392.

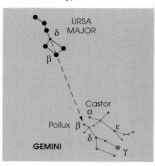

Finding Gemini in the sky is straightforward: extend the line joining δ (Delta) Ursae Majoris (Megrez) to β (Beta) Ursae Majoris (Merak) and you come straight to Pollux, one of the constellation's two brightest stars. ▷

δ (Delta) GEMINORUM (WASAT)

Mag 3.5 & 8

This star, 59 light years away, was discovered in 1829 to be a double. The two components appear only 6.3″ apart, but the distance between them is in fact about 100 AU. The smaller star takes about 1,200 years to orbit the larger one. In February 1930, Clyde Tombaugh discovered Pluto on photographic plates that showed the dwarf planet passing by δ (Delta) Geminorum.

M35

Mag 5.1

This open cluster, most spectacular in binoculars, is in the westernmost part of the constellation. Its overall magnitude makes it visible to the naked eye, though only on a very clear night with no light pollution. With the smallest of instruments a hundred or so stars can be seen. The cluster is 2,700 light years distant, and its apparent diameter of 30′ means that it is actually 30 light years across. Close to it in our skies is another, much more distant open cluster: NGC 2158.

△ *The open clusters M35 and NGC 2158.*

174

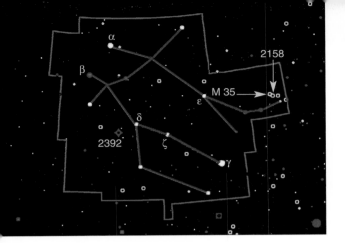

ζ (Zeta) GEMINORUM (MEKBUDA)

Mag 3.7 to 4.2

This is one of the brightest stars of the type known as Cepheid variables. Its cycle lasts slightly more than 10 days, and during this period it goes from magnitude 3.7 to magnitude 4.2 and back. Mekbuda has two companion stars: one of magnitude 8, 96.5″ away, and the other of magnitude 11, at a distance of 87.7″. However, neither of these is linked with it gravitationally.

NGC 2158

Mag 8.6

Another star cluster that is not hard to find, located 30′ southwest of M35. But a telescope is needed, and in an amateur instrument this cluster still looks like nothing more than a faint nebulous shape. None of its stars has an individual magnitude greater than 16, which explains why it cannot be seen other than as a "cloud." It is not easy to observe, and though it seems close to M35 it is in fact 16,000 light years away, which is nearly six times as distant.

NGC 2392 (CLOWN'S HEAD or ESKIMO NEBULA)

Mag 10

This planetary nebula, not easy to find with a small astronomical instrument, has been made famous through photographs obtained by large telescopes, which reveal its extraordinary shape. As its names suggest, it looks like a face, with a central star marking the nose. The nebula was discovered in 1787 by William Herschel. It is difficult to distinguish from a star because, although the whole object extends over 44″, only the central part (lit by a magnitude 10 star) is bright enough to be seen in a small telescope. The Clown's Head is 3,000 light years from the Solar System.

VISIBLE: fall (on Meridian at 21:00 in mid-December)

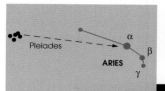

This is one of the constellations of the Zodiac, and is rich in double and multiple stars.

△ Aries is not difficult to find: its two principal stars lie to the west of the Pleiades cluster (which is in the constellation Taurus).

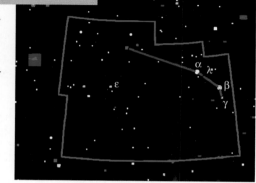

γ (Gamma) ARIETIS (MESARTHIM)

Mag
4.5 & 4.5

This is one of the most famous of double stars, discovered in 1664 by chance, as an astronomer was tracking a comet. Over three centuries, the angular distance between the two components of this physical binary system has decreased from 8.6″ to 7.8″. It is some 160 light years away, and a small telescope is all that is needed to observe it with ease.

ε (Epsilon) ARIETIS

Mag
5.2 & 5.5

This physical binary provides a good test of observers and their equipment: the two stars should be distinguishable in a 3-inch (75mm) telescope. They are 155 light years distant, and separated by just 1.5″.

λ (Lambda) ARIETIS

Mag
5 & 7.5

There are some double stars that can be observed with binoculars, and this system is one of them. The two components are 37.4″ apart.

VISIBLE: fall (on Meridian at 21:00 in mid-December)

TRIANGULUM
Alpheratz
β
γ
α
β

Great Square
of Pegasus

The ancient constellation Triangulum is not a large one, but it does contain the well known galaxy M33, which with M31 belongs to our Local Group.

β
γ
M 33
α

△ *This is a small constellation without any very bright stars, but with major landmarks nearby. The line from β (Beta) Pegasi to Alpheratz (along the Great Square of Pegasus), extended for about the same distance again, will lead to the western boundary of the constellation.*

6 TRIANGULI

Mag
5 & 6.5

This double star is a physical binary over 200 light years away, with one yellow and one blue component that are 3.8″ apart.

M33

Mag
5.5

This spiral galaxy, which we see "from above," is one of the best known, since it is very close to the Milky Way (2.4 million light years). Although its overall magnitude is estimated at 5.5, it is still very hard to find with a small telescope, for it is very spread out (1° × 35′). Whatever instrument is used, the best time to look for it is on a really dark, moonless night. With a 6-inch (150 mm) or larger telescope, it is possible to see the nucleus surrounded by a faint glow from the spiral arms, though the pattern of these is hard to make out. To see some of the individual stars and nebulae within the galaxy, you will need a 10-inch (250 mm) telescope.

The spiral galaxy M33, 2.4 million light years away. ▷

CANIS MINOR

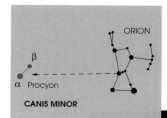

CANIS MINOR

Canis Minor is not a particularly rich constellation. It has a few double and variable stars, but no nebulae and no galaxies of magnitude greater than 13.

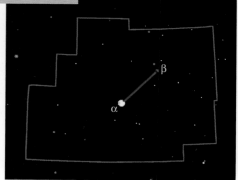

△ *The principal star in Canis Minor, Procyon, is one of the brightest in this part of the sky, making the constellation fairly easy to find. It lies east of Orion and south of Gemini.*

α (Alpha) CANIS MINORIS (PROCYON)

Mag 0.4 & 10.8

Procyon is the eighth most brilliant star in the sky, and is part of a double system. It is also, at 11.4 light years distant, one of the closest stars to the Sun. Because of Procyon's brightness, it is extremely difficult with amateur equipment to make out its magnitude 10.8 companion, which is only 4″ of arc away. A more powerful telescope is needed to reveal this star, which takes a little over 40 years to orbit Procyon. Procyon has an apparent motion among the stars of 1.25″ per year: with the aid of a powerful telescope, it is possible to detect its movement over the course of a few years.

14 CANIS MINORIS

Mag 5.4, 7 & 8

This is a star that can be seen with the naked eye. It has two fainter (magnitude 7 and 8) companions, one over 1′ 30″ and the other over 2′ away. The triple system can be resolved with any amateur equipment.

Visible: winter (on Meridian at 21:00 in mid-March)

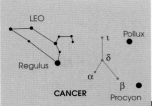

Cancer, the Crab, is a fairly extensive constellation, but has no very bright stars to distinguish it. It contains an interesting multiple system and two open clusters, one of which ranks among the brightest.

△ *Cancer is a constellation in the Zodiac. It lies on the ecliptic between Leo and Gemini, within a triangle formed by Pollux (in Gemini), Procyon (in Canis Minor), and Regulus.*

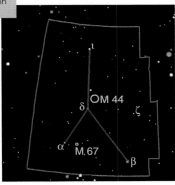

ζ (Zeta) CANCRI

Mag 5.5 & 6

This star was reported as a double in 1756, and further observations revealed in 1781 that it is in fact a triple system: today, it is one of the best known. The component closest to the principal star orbits it every 59.6 years, and its angular separation of 0.6″ to 1.2″ represents a distance similar to that between Uranus and the Sun. The further component (5.8″ away) takes 1,150 years to complete one revolution. The system is 70 light years from Earth.

M44 (PRAESEPE)

Mag 3.1

Praesepe, or the Beehive Cluster, is one of the closest (at a distance of 520 light years) and brightest open clusters that we know. It can be seen with the naked eye, and in binoculars or a telescope with a wide field of view it makes a splendid sight.

M67

Mag 6.9

Another open cluster, this time 2,600 light years away, 9° south of M44. M67 has over 200 stars in an area 30′ across.

LEO

As well as a fine double star and an impressive variable, Leo contains some relatively close galaxies that are visible in binoculars.

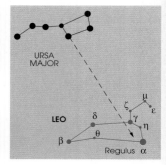

Leo is an easy constellation to find, lying just below Ursa Major. More precisely, a line from Megrez to Phekda in Ursa Major points almost exactly to Regulus, the principal star in Leo. ▷

γ (Gamma) LEONIS (ALGIEBA)

Mag 2.5 & 3.5

The Arabic name of this star is thought to mean "the Lion's forehead." The principal star has a companion, just 4.3″ away, which orbits it in 618 years, making this an interesting physical binary system for amateurs to observe. Algieba is 125 light years away. There is also a third component at an angular distance of 4.9′, though this is not gravitationally linked to the other two.

R LEONIS

Mag 5.2 to 10.5

This is one of the brightest long-period variable stars in the sky. At its maximum, it can easily be observed with the naked eye, but it has quite a long period: 313 days. However, a small amateur instrument is all that is needed to show it even at its faintest. R Leonis is located 5° to the west of α (Alpha) Leonis (Regulus), and its red light reaches us after a 3,000-year journey through space.

M65

Mag 9

Positioned halfway between θ (Theta) Leonis (Chort) and ι (Iota) Leonis is this superb spiral galaxy, which is approximately 33 million light years away from the Solar System. From Earth, we see the galaxy sideways on, so that it looks (in a small amateur telescope, at any rate) rather like an elongated nebula. It is easily confused with M66 (see next page), which is only 21′ of arc away, but M65 is further west – or to the left, in the inverted field of an astronomical telescope. It may just be possible to make out these two galaxies with the aid of a pair of binoculars.

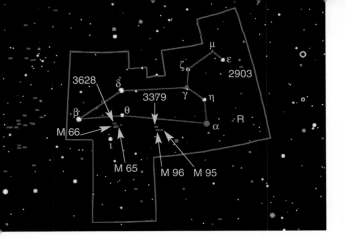

M66

Mag 9

This galaxy is right next door to M65, and in fact they are only 180,000 light years apart. It has asymmetrical spiral arms, though these are not easy to see in a medium-sized telescope. There is a third galaxy located 35′ to the north of M66, which is larger but not so bright: this is NGC 3628 (see overleaf).

◁ Galaxies M66 (bottom right), M65 (top right) and NGC 3628 (left) are very close together in the sky, separated by only a few minutes of arc.

M96

Mag 9

This is a spiral galaxy which we see "from above." It is a near neighbor of M95: they are only 400,000 light years apart. The apparent diameter of M96 is only 6′. In a small telescope or a pair of binoculars, it appears as a mere whitish blob.

Leo

M95

Mag
10

This galaxy is 34 million light years away, and of the barred spiral type. Its nucleus is very bright compared with its arms, which are not easy to see with a small instrument.

△ The barred spiral galaxy M95. Only the bright nucleus can be seen clearly with amateur equipment.

NGC 2903

Mag
9

This galaxy is one of the brightest in Leo. It is a long way from the others, and is the only one in front of the Lion's mane. It is a spiral galaxy, seen almost exactly from above, and 23 million light years away. In an amateur instrument it can be seen as an oval shape.

NGC 3379 (M105)

Mag
9

Although Messier's list ends at the number 104, this galaxy is sometimes referred to as M105. It is quite easy to find from M96, which lies just 48′ to the south-southwest. It is elliptical in shape.

NGC 3628

Mag
9.5

This galaxy is seen exactly edge on, and a dark line of dust gives it a stripe along its entire length. The galaxy's slender shape can be made out with a small telescope. M66, M65, and NGC 3628 are among the brightest of all galaxies, making them good objects for those with small telescopes to observe.

VISIBLE: summer (on Meridian at 21:00 in mid-September)

A tiny, faint constellation, the Little Horse is remarkable only for its poverty. Its most interesting object is a galaxy of magnitude 13, so there is very little for the amateur astronomer here, apart from an optical double which can be resolved with the naked eye.

△ *Equuleus is just below Delphinus, or more precisely 18° east of the brilliant star Deneb in the constellation Cygnus.*

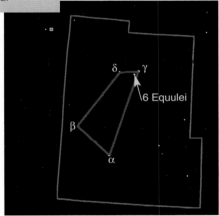

γ (Gamma) EQUULEI

Mag 4.8 & 6

This star is very close in the sky to another, 6 Equulei, of magnitude 6: the separation between them is 6′. Resolving these two with the naked eye is a good test of eyesight, especially if you have already succeeded in resolving the two components of ζ (Zeta) Ursae Majoris (Mizar and Alcor) in the Big Dipper, which are 11′ apart. 6 Equulei has a magnitude 11 companion, 2″ away, but this can only be made out with a 2½-inch (60 mm) telescope.

δ (Delta) EQUULEI

Mag 5.5 & 10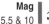

The two principal components of this triple system are very difficult to distinguish, since they are only 0.35″ apart. The third component, though much fainter, is at a distance of 64″ and easy to see.

PEGASUS

VISIBLE: fall (on Meridian at 21:00 in mid-October)

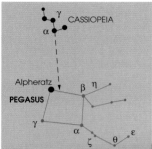

Pegasus, the Winged Horse, is a large constellation and has a variety of objects for amateurs to observe: a rich offering of double stars, globular clusters, and galaxies.

△ *Alpheratz, the brightest star in the Great Square of Pegasus (though it actually belongs to the constellation Andromeda), lies almost exactly on a long extension of the line from γ (Gamma) to α (Alpha) Cassiopeiae.*

51 PEGASI

Mag 5.6

This is a star of the same type as the Sun, with nothing remarkable to see: its only point of interest is that a planet just a little smaller than Jupiter orbits it with a period of 4 days and 6 hours.

M15

Mag 6

One of the most compact and brightest of globular clusters, M15 is 30,000 light years away and can be observed with any instrument, even a pair of binoculars.

NGC 7331

Mag 9.5

This is a spiral galaxy which we see at an oblique angle. It is 55 million light years away. In 1959, a supernova of magnitude 12.7 was observed in one of its spiral arms.

Visible: fall (on Meridian at 21:00 in mid-November)

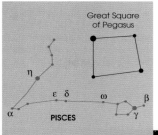

The constellation Pisces is fairly large and contains some fine double stars, as well as a splendid spiral galaxy which we see full on.

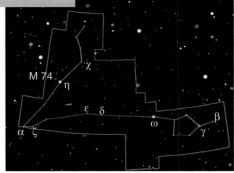

△ *Pisces, the Fishes, curves right round the eastern and southern sides of the Great Square of Pegasus, so this is not a difficult constellation to find.*

α (Alpha) PISCIUM

Mag 4.3 & 5.2

This star, 130 light years away, has a companion of magnitude 5.2 at an angular distance of 1.9″, which orbits it in 933 years. A 3-inch (75 mm) telescope is needed to resolve the pair.

ζ (Zeta) PISCIUM

Mag 5.6 & 6.5

Another double star, but this one can be resolved with binoculars. The components are 23″ apart and lie exactly on the ecliptic, which means that they are sometimes occulted by bodies in the Solar System.

M74

Mag 9.7

This spiral galaxy is one of the most difficult Messier objects to observe. Look for it only in a really dark sky, at 1° 20′ east-northeast of the star η (Eta) Piscium, and it may be seen as a blob, 6′ in diameter, that comes and goes. It is 40 million light years away and in fact measures over 100,000 light years across.

CETUS

Alpheratz
Great Square of Pegasus
γ
α γ
CETUS
δ
o
η
ζ θ
β

Cetus, the Whale, is a large constellation on the celestial equator, so it is easily seen from the northern hemisphere. Its best known object is the variable star Mira.

△ *To find Cetus, extend the line joining Alpheratz to γ (Gamma) Pegasi in the Great Square of Pegasus.*

o (Omicron) CETI (MIRA)

Mag
3 to 10.1

Mira, whose name means "Wonderful," is one of the best known variables. Discovered in 1596, it varies from magnitude 3 or 4 to 10.1, taking 331 days to complete the cycle. Just occasionally it even reaches magnitude 2.

γ (Gamma) CETI (KAFFALJIDHMA)

Mag
3.5 & 7.3

This star, 82 light years away, has a companion at an angular distance of just 2.8″, which makes it a good test of an amateur telescope.

M77

Mag
9

Situated 1° southeast of δ (Delta) Ceti, this fine galaxy is one of the few whose spiral arms can be seen with a small telescope. It is 57 million light years away from the Solar System.

VISIBLE: winter (on Meridian at 21:00 in early January)

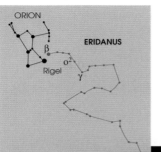

ORION
β
ERIDANUS
Rigel
o²
γ

This huge constellation was supposed to represent one of the rivers of the Underworld. It cannot all be seen from mid-northern latitudes (above 25° north), but most of it is visible, including some galaxies.

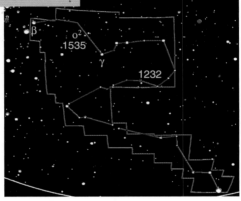

△ *The bright star Rigel in Orion marks the boundary with Eridanus, but this constellation's pattern is not easy to recognize.*

o² (Omicron²) ERIDANI

Mag
4.5, 9.5 & 11

This is in fact a triple star system. Component B is 83″ from component A and orbits it in 7,000 years. Component C orbits B in 248 years and is only 9″ from it in our sky.

NGC 1232

Mag
9

This spiral galaxy, which we see directly from above, extends over 8′ of arc.

NGC 1535

Mag
10

A planetary nebula 4° east of γ (Gamma) Eridani, NGC 1535 is 2,000 light years away and appears as a small disk 20″ across. The central star is of magnitude 11.8.

ORION

The constellation Orion, clearly visible above the southern horizon, is known chiefly for its great nebula M42, which can be seen without difficulty by the naked eye.

Framed by the brilliant stars Sirius (in Canis Major) and Aldebaran (in Taurus), Orion itself contains bright stars such as Betelgeuse, Rigel, and Bellatrix, making it one of the sky's major landmarks. ▷

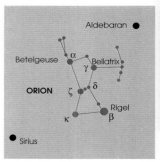

α (Alpha) ORIONIS (BETELGEUSE)

Mag 0.5

This is a giant star, over 600 times the diameter of the Sun – and it could blow up at any moment. Betelgeuse is one of those stars which will end as supernovae. When that happens, it will light the night sky for weeks, as brightly as the full moon, and will even be visible in the daytime. Then it will "disappear," becoming a neutron star which hardly shines at all. Recent measurements by the Hipparcos satellite put it 427 light years away.

σ (Sigma) ORIONIS

Mag 4, 6, 7.5, 10 & 6.5

Just below ζ (Zeta) Orionis, the first star in Orion's belt, this is a quintuple star system 1,400 light years from Earth. Apart from the principal star's closest companion, only 0.25″ away, the others are easy to distinguish, at angular distances of 11″, 13″, and 43″.

M42 (ORION NEBULA)

Mag 4

The Orion Nebula, or Great Nebula in Orion, is an immense cloud of gas 1,500 light years away, and a favorite object with novice astronomers. It can be seen with the naked eye, and makes a splendid sight in a pair of

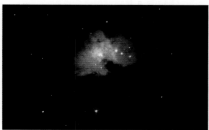

binoculars. A 2¹/₂-inch (60 mm) telescope with low magnification will show it as a large white patch, roughly quadri-lateral in shape. Using a 5-inch (130 mm) tele-scope makes a number of

◁ *M42, the Orion Nebula*

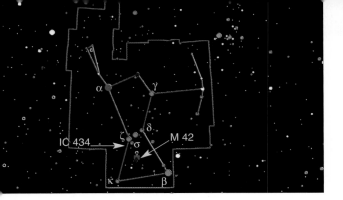

excrescences visible, and an 8-inch (200 mm) or larger instrument reveals plenty of detail within the cloudy areas. At the center of the nebula is a group of four young stars that can be made out with a very small instrument. This formation is known as the Trapezium, and beginners find it helpful as a way of getting used to the appearance of particular angular distances, which they will often encounter when viewing double stars. The two closest stars in the Trapezium are 8.7″ apart.

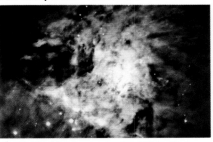

△ This shot shows the central region of M42, which is often overexposed in photographs covering the whole field of the nebula.

IC 434 and the HORSEHEAD NEBULA

Mag ind

Extending below ζ (Zeta) Orionis is the bright nebula IC 434. Protruding into its western edge is the small (6′ × 4′), dark Horsehead Nebula, famously shaped like a chess knight. Amateurs will not be able to see this at all. With a good 10-inch (250 mm) telescope and excellent viewing conditions, the most that can be seen is a thin, pale line against the background of the sky – nothing that looks at all like a horse. The dark cloud of gas shows up only in long photographic exposures.

The Horsehead Nebula (center below), a splendid object, but only to be seen in photographs. ▷

HYDRA

Visible: spring (on Meridian at 21:00 in early May)

Hydra is a very long, thin constellation, extending from Libra all the way to Monoceros, the Unicorn. Seen from high northern latitudes, it stays very low over the horizon. It contains a number of objects of different kinds that are well worth observing: a tight double star, an open cluster, a globular cluster, a spiral galaxy, and a planetary nebula.

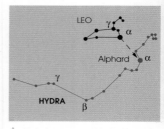

△ Hydra is not easy to identify. Extend the line joining γ (Gamma) Leonis to α (Alpha) Leonis (Regulus) to find Alphard, which is the principal star in Hydra.

β (Beta) HYDRAE

Mag 4.7 & 5.5

This, the second star in the constellation, is a physical binary with components barely 0.9″ apart. Though the system can be seen with the naked eye, resolving the two stars is a good test of a 6-inch (150 mm) telescope.

R HYDRAE

Mag 3 to 11

This is a variable star with a long period (390 days). When the giant star is at its faintest, it gives 1,600 times less light than it does at its brightest. However, it remains visible at all times to observers equipped with a 2½-inch (60 mm) telescope.

M48

Mag 5.8

This is an open cluster, not too difficult to find with binoculars, but at the limit of visibility for the naked eye. In a telescope it makes a splendid sight: the cluster has no fewer than 50 stars above magnitude 13, spread over 50′ of sky. It is 2,000 light years away from us, and its actual diameter is over 20 light years.

M68

Mag 8.2

A globular cluster 31,000 light years away, M68 is not one of the most spectacular. With its apparent diameter of 12.5′, in most telescopes it remains mostly unresolved into stars. A 6-inch (150 mm) instrument only barely enables a few to be distinguished. In higher northern latitudes this object hardly rises above the horizon, which does not make it any easier to observe.

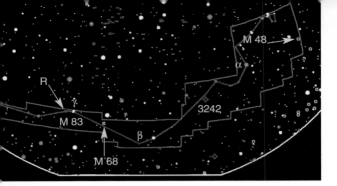

M83

Mag 7

This is one of the brightest galaxies in the southern sky. A medium-sized telescope (around 6 inches or 150 mm) is enough to reveal hints of its spiral structure, seen "from above." However, above 45° north it becomes a tricky object to observe, because it does not rise far above the horizon.

It is about 17 million light years from the Solar System and about 50,000 light years across. A very large number of supernovae have been observed within this galaxy: no fewer than four have been seen in 50 years.

The spiral galaxy M83, as seen in a large telescope. ▷

NGC 3242
(GHOST OF JUPITER NEBULA)

Mag 9

Although this planetary nebula is in a rather inconvenient part of the sky for observers in Europe and the northern United States, it is one of the most interesting to observe. The central star (magnitude 11.4) is theoretically visible with a telescope with an aperture as small as 3 inches (75 mm), but because of the "backdrop" of luminous gas, it is actually difficult to see. The ovoid envelope of gas surrounding it is divided into two "rings," the inner one being brighter and 26″ × 16″ in apparent size. The other, outer ring is much less bright and extends over 40″ of arc. An 8 to 10-inch (200 to 250 mm) telescope shows both structures well. The nebula's distance is around 2,600 light years.

VISIBLE: winter (on Meridian at 21:00 in mid-February)

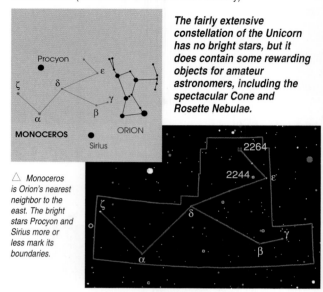

The fairly extensive constellation of the Unicorn has no bright stars, but it does contain some rewarding objects for amateur astronomers, including the spectacular Cone and Rosette Nebulae.

△ *Monoceros is Orion's nearest neighbor to the east. The bright stars Procyon and Sirius more or less mark its boundaries.*

β (Beta) MONOCEROTIS

Mag
4.7, 5.2 & 5.6

This is a physical triple system 30 light years away, and one of the finest and easiest to observe. The two secondary components are 7.4″ and 2.8″ from the principal star.

NGC 2244 (ROSETTE NEBULA)

Mag
4.8

In a really dark sky, this open cluster 2,600 light years away can be seen with the naked eye; with binoculars, it is visible on almost any clear night. It has nine stars of magnitude 6, still enveloped in a fine nebula, the material from which the stars are being formed. The nebula itself, however, can only be seen with very large telescopes or in long-exposure photographs.

NGC 2264 (CONE NEBULA in the CHRISTMAS TREE CLUSTER)

Mag
10

This nebula, observable with a small astronomical instrument, is peculiar in that its luminosity varies. In fact, it is the central star illuminating it that is an irregular variable. The strange behavior of the nebula was first noted by Edwin Hubble. It covers 50′ of sky and is 2,600 light years away.

VISIBLE: winter (on Meridian at 21:00 in mid-February)

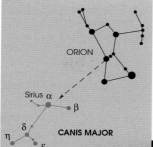

Canis Major, in the low southern latitudes, can easily be seen by observers in the northern hemisphere. Its foremost star, Sirius, is the brightest in the whole night sky; near it is a fine open cluster.

△ *Finding Canis Major is no problem at all. The three stars of Orion's belt lead directly to Sirius, a star outshone only by the Sun, the Moon, Venus, Jupiter, and Mars when in opposition.*

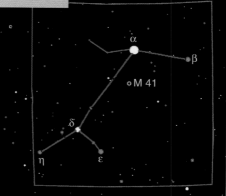

α (Alpha) CANIS MAJORIS (SIRIUS)

Mag −1.5 & 8.7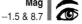

There is no advantage in observing the brightest star in the sky with a telescope: it is still only a brilliant point of light. But in fact, this star 8.6 light years away is a binary system: a white dwarf orbits it every 50 years. Amateurs can only hope to distinguish this faint companion against the dazzling brightness of Sirius when it is at maximum separation (11″), and even then a telescope with an aperture of at least 10 inches (250 mm) is needed, as well as a perfectly calm sky. And patience: the next maximum separation will be in 2025.

M41

Mag 4.5

This is an open cluster, 4° south of Sirius and 2,300 light years away. It is an easy target and makes a wonderful sight in a small telescope.

LEPUS

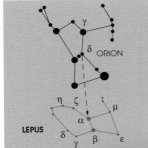

Lepus, the Hare, is no treasure chest for amateur astronomers, although those who specialize in variable stars can follow the changes in R Leporis over a year or more. The constellation also contains a globular cluster of moderate brightness.

△ *Lepus is just below Orion. Take a line from γ (Gamma) Orionis to δ (Delta) Orionis, and extend it to reach the neighborhood of α (Alpha) Leporis.*

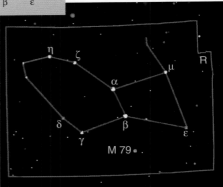

R LEPORIS

Mag
5.5 to 11.7

At its brightest, this variable star (sometimes called Hind's Crimson Star) is just detectable by the naked eye. Over an average period of 432 days, it fades to just one-hundredth of its maximum brilliance, and then brightens again. It is some 1,500 light years from our Solar System.

M79

Mag
8

Trace a line between the constellation's two brightest stars, and continue it southward for a similar distance, to find this globular cluster 43,000 light years away. It covers about 8' and is not one of the easiest in which to see individual stars: for that, an 8 to 10-inch (200 to 250 mm) telescope is needed.

SEXTANS

VISIBLE: spring (on Meridian at 21:00 in mid-April)

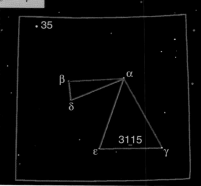

This southern constellation has few objects of interest to the amateur: only one double star and one galaxy are really worthy of attention. The best time to observe Sextans is in the spring.

△ It is not difficult to find Sextans in the sky, since it is just south of the bright star Regulus, in the constellation Leo. Making out its pattern, on the other hand, is more difficult: there are no particularly bright stars, the brightest being only of magnitude 4.5.

35 SEXTANTIS

Mag 6.5 & 7.5

The two components of this double are only 6.8″ apart. The system, which cannot be seen with the naked eye, is in the northeast corner of Sextans.

NGC 3115 (SPINDLE GALAXY)

Mag 9

This elliptical galaxy is seen by us edge on, which gives it a distinctive lens-like shape. It is 25 million light years away and about 30,000 light years across, and should be visible in a 2-inch (50 mm) telescope in a clear sky.

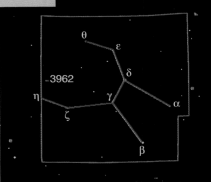

Crater, the Cup, is one of the southern constellations that can easily be seen in spring by observers in the northern hemisphere. But it has no galaxies or nebulae that make rewarding targets for an amateur's medium-sized telescope.

△ *Crater's principal star, δ (Delta) Crateris (not α), is of magnitude 3.8. It can easily be found by taking the line from δ (Delta) Leonis to θ (Theta) Leonis and extending it six times, still in a southerly direction. The "cup" pattern of Crater is not clear, because some of its stars are so faint.*

γ (Gamma) CRATERIS

Mag
4.1 & 9.6

This double star is the only object in the constellation that is easy for amateur astronomers to observe. It is 78 light years from Earth, and the two components are 5.2″ apart.

NGC 3962

Mag
10.5

This is an unremarkable elliptical galaxy, but the only one in Crater that an amateur with a telescope of 6 inches (150 mm) or less can expect to see. It looks like a pale blob, covering about 3′ on the constellation's eastern boundary. Coordinates: RA = 11h 54.6m, Dec. = 13° 57.5′

VISIBLE: spring (on Meridian at 21:00 in early May)

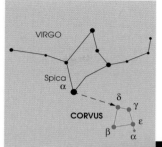

VIRGO

Spica
α

δ
γ
CORVUS
ε
β
α

Corvus, next door to Crater, contains one of the sky's great curiosities: two galaxies "colliding." However, this is not an easy object for amateurs to observe. The double star δ (Delta) Corvi, on the other hand, is one of the easiest to resolve.

△ *The four principal stars of Corvus form a trapezium that can be found west of α (Alpha) Virginis (Spica), the brightest star in the constellation Virgo.*

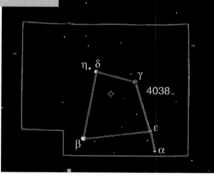

η. δ
γ
4038
ε
β
α

δ (Delta) CORVI (ALGORAB)

Mag 3 & 8.5

The first astronomer to notice this double star was John Herschel, in 1823. Though its components are as much as 24.2″ apart, this is a true physical binary, 88 light years from us.

NGC 4038 (RING-TAILED GALAXY or THE ANTENNAE)

Mag 11

There are in fact two galaxies here. Their names derive from the two filaments of stars emerging from them under the force of their gravitational interaction. Unfortunately, these are too faint to be seen with the equipment available to an amateur, which will at best show the two galaxies looking like an upside-down question mark.

LIBRA

VISIBLE: summer (on Meridian at 21:00 in early July)

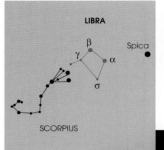

This constellation, part of the Zodiac, is quite extensive but not very distinguished. It is made up of rather faint stars, forming a pattern which is not easy to recognize.

△ *Libra is just in front of the head of the Scorpion, easy to see because of Antares. It is bordered on the west by Virgo, whose principal star, Spica, is easily recognized.*

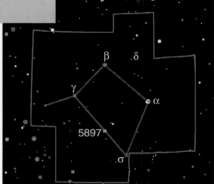

α (Alpha) LIBRAE (ZUBENELGENUBI)

Mag 3 & 5

The Arabic name of this star means the "Southern Claw" (the Northern Claw being Zubeneschamali, β (Beta) Librae). It is an optical double which can be resolved even with binoculars, since the angular separation is 3′ 51″. The brighter component is only 78 light years away from Earth.

δ (Delta) LIBRAE

Mag 4.8 to 5.9

This is an eclipsing variable of the same kind as Algol: a binary star whose components are too close to be resolved with a telescope. Every 2 days, 7h, 41m, the darker star largely eclipses the brighter one, reducing the whole system to its minimum magnitude in the space of 6 hours.

NGC 5897

Mag 8.6

This globular cluster is 40,000 light years away and has the peculiarity of being rather poor in stars.

VISIBLE: summer (on Meridian at 21:00 in mid-August)

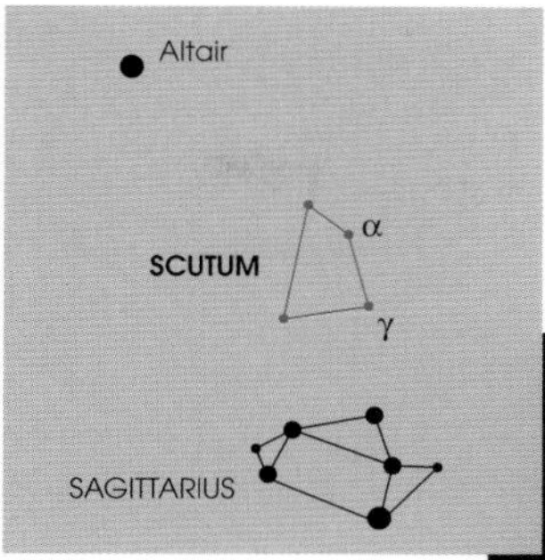

Scutum , the Shield, was created in the seventeenth century. It can be seen on summer evenings, and contains variable stars and some very fine open clusters.

△ Scutum lies just above Sagittarius and below Aquila, which contains the bright star Altair, one of the Summer Triangle of stars.

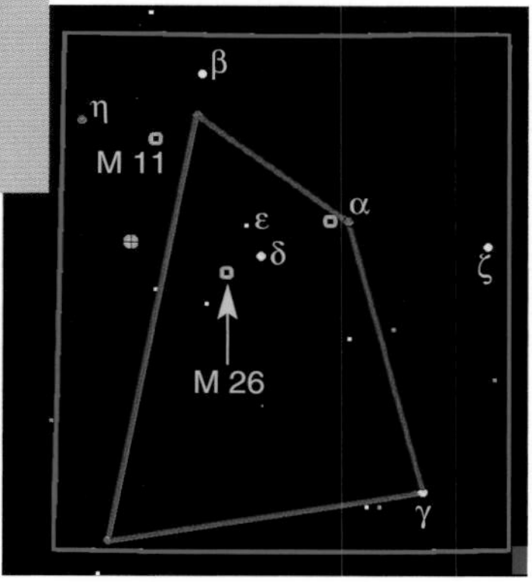

δ (Delta) SCUTI

Mag
5.0 to 5.2

This is a variable, changing by 0.2 of a magnitude over a period of 4 hours and 39 minutes. Only 52″ away is another star, of magnitude 9.2, which however has no gravitational connection with it.

M11 (WILD DUCK CLUSTER)

Mag
5.8

This splendid open cluster, whose fan-shaped central portion has been likened to wild ducks in flight, is in theory visible to the naked eye. However, the sky needs to be really dark. In the smallest pair of binoculars it can be seen clearly, and in a small telescope it offers an exciting spectacle. With a 10-inch (250 mm) instrument, some 100 stars can be seen out of the 500 which it contains. The cluster is 5,600 light years away.

M26

Mag
8

Another open cluster which can be seen with amateur equipment: it is 5,050 light years away.

OPHIUCHUS

Visible: summer (on Meridian at 21:00 in mid-July)

This very spread-out constellation contains several globular clusters. It also includes the fastest-moving star in the sky (the one with the greatest apparent motion).

There is no obvious alignment by which to find Ophiuchus. The constellation's shape is not easy to make out, but it is bordered by Sagittarius, Scorpius, and Aquila (the Eagle), which contains Altair, one of the three stars of the Summer Triangle. ▷

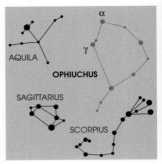

70 OPHIUCHI

Mag 4 & 6

This star, 4° 23′ away from γ (Gamma) Ophiuchi, is one of the best known of the double stars. It was identified in 1779 by William Herschel. The second component takes a little less than 88 years to make one revolution around the primary star. Their separation therefore varies noticeably over the course of a decade. They can be as close as 1.7″, but by 2000 they were about 5″ apart. The system is only 16.5 light years from Earth.

BARNARD'S STAR

Mag 9.5

This rather faint (magnitude 9.5) red dwarf is the nearest star to the Sun after the Alpha Centauri system: only 6 light years distant. It is also the one with the greatest apparent movement across the sky. It moves by 10.31″ each year, so that it is possible, over the course of a few years, to detect the change in its position with an ordinary telescope. The main difficulty is finding it. It lies less than 1° to the west of 66 Ophiuchi, and is a faint star that can be distinguished from its neighbors only with the help of a detailed sky atlas.
Coordinates: RA = 17h 57.8m, Dec. = 04° 41′ (year 2000).

M9

Mag 7.9

This globular cluster is one of the closest to the center of the Milky Way, located only 7,000 light years from the central bulge. On the other hand, it is 25,000 light years from Earth. Though not one of the most spectacular globular clusters, it is one that can be observed with any amateur instrument.

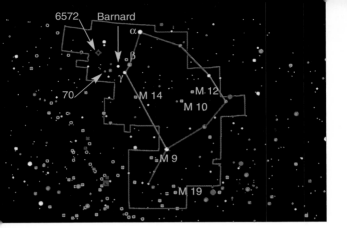

M10

 Mag 6.6

Easy to find with binoculars, this globular cluster 14,000 light years away is in the center of the constellation. A 6-inch (150 mm) telescope is sufficient to resolve some of its individual stars.

M12

  Mag 6.6

Not far (3° 23′) from M10 is another globular cluster, M12. The two objects are in reality quite close, only 4,000 light years apart. M12, which extends over an angular distance of 14′ 30″, is not particularly dense, so individual stars in the cluster can be distinguished with the help of a fairly small telescope.

M14

 Mag 7.6

Another globular cluster, just to the east of M10 and M12, fainter but richer in stars than the other two. It is also further away: around 33,000 light years from Earth.

M19

 Mag 7.2

This is a good globular cluster for amateurs to observe, and one of the few oval ones. M19 is thought to be a little further away than M14.

NGC 6572

 Mag 9

This planetary nebula is known for the pronounced blue-green color of its 15″ disk. It is not easy to find, hiding against the background of the sky just over 2° southeast of 71 Ophiuchi.

VIRGO

Visible: summer (on Meridian at 21:00 in mid-May)

A large constellation of the Zodiac, Virgo is a treasure trove of galaxies, and the northern part of the constellation is occupied by one of the closest galaxy clusters in the whole universe.

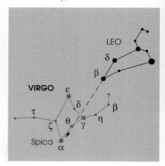

Virgo immediately follows Leo along the line of the ecliptic. A straight line from δ (Delta) to β (Beta) Leonis points directly to Spica, the brightest star in Virgo and the fifteenth brightest in the whole sky. ▷

γ (Gamma) VIRGINIS (PORRIMA)

Mag
3.5 & 3.5

Porrima is one of the finest double stars. The two components, a little over 1.5″ apart in 2000, are of the same magnitude, which makes them easier to observe. They orbit each other in 169 years, but the orbit is highly eccentric. In 2000 they can be separated in a 4-inch (100 mm) telescope, but when at their closest, around 2005, a 10-inch (250 mm) instrument will be necessary. Thereafter, as the components move apart, the system will provide a check for telescopes of all sizes.

VIRGO CLUSTER

Mag
ind

All the galaxies detailed below belong to a galaxy cluster that is about 45 million light years distant from our Solar System. With a small amateur telescope, even the brightest galaxies in the cluster can be seen only as small, diffuse blobs.

M49

Mag
8

An elliptical galaxy extending over 8′ and having a diameter of about 50,000 light years. It appears as a round blob in a 3-inch (75 mm) instrument.

M58

Mag
10

A good sky map and a little patience are needed to pick out M58 among all the other galaxies that fill the northern part of this constellation. This is a barred spiral galaxy, and its shape can be made out with an 8-inch (200 mm) telescope. The galaxy's diameter is probably in the region of 50,000 light years.

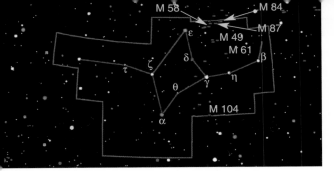

M61

Among these elliptical galaxies, M61 offers the sight of spiral arms seen full on. However, they can only be detected in a powerful instrument.

M84

This is the westernmost galaxy in the group on the boundary between Virgo and Coma Berenices. It is a bright elliptical galaxy about 25,000 light years across.

M87

M87 is a giant elliptical galaxy with a total mass 790,000 million times that of the Sun. A powerful jet of matter is streaming out of its nucleus. Observations by the Hubble Space Telescope in 1994 indicated that the cause of this expulsion of matter is probably a massive black hole. The telescopes available to amateurs show this galaxy only as an oval blob; the jet cannot be seen.

M104 (SOMBRERO GALAXY)

This is a spiral galaxy seen almost exactly edge on. It owes its name to the band of gas and dust across its center. Even a small telescope can reveal its elongated shape, while a 6-inch (150 mm) instrument makes it just possible to see the dark stripe. This galaxy is one of those that enabled early twentieth-century astronomers to deduce that the universe is expanding. It is not a member of the Virgo Cluster, lying rather closer at around 35 million light years.

The Sombrero Galaxy, one of the first to have its speed of recession from Earth measured. ▷

SERPENS

Visible: summer (on Meridian at 21:00 in mid-July)

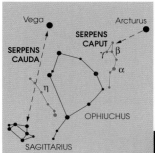

Serpens is an odd constellation, because it is cut in two by another constellation, Ophiuchus.

◁ *The Serpent's head (Caput) is east of Arcturus, on an extension of the line from Alioth to Benetnash in Ursa Major. The tail (Cauda) is above Sagittarius, in the direction of the bright star Vega.*

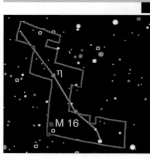

M5

Mag 5.8

This is one of the loveliest globular clusters in the sky. It is 26,000 light years away and makes a good target for amateurs, even those equipped only with binoculars.

M16 and IC 4703 (EAGLE NEBULA)

Mag 8.2

M16 is an open cluster of about 60 stars, some 8,000 light years distant and surrounded by the Eagle Nebula. In this magnificent cloud of gas and dust,

new stars are being born. A good 6-inch (150 mm) telescope shows some detail, while an 8-inch (200 mm) one begins to reveal the way the edges of the bright cloud are "nibbled" by dark clouds.

◁ *IC 4703, a seedbed of stars*

VISIBLE: summer (on Meridian at 21:00 in early September)

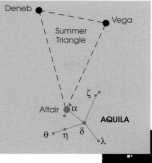

Aquila is a splendid summer constellation, but in spite of its size it has relatively few interesting objects to offer the amateur astronomer. Although it is on the Galactic equator, it contains no nebulae.

△ *Aquila cannot be missed: Altair, its brightest star, is itself a landmark, since it is one of the vertices of the Summer Triangle.*

α (Alpha) AQUILAE (ALTAIR)

Mag
0.8, 9.6 & 10.1

This, the most brilliant star in Aquila, is also the twelfth brightest in the whole sky. It is in fact an optical triple, for there are two faint stars lying 190″ and 238″ away. Altair is 16.8 light years from the Sun.

η (Eta) AQUILAE

Mag
3.7 to 4.5

This star is one of the brightest of the type of variable star known as a Cepheid variable. It has a period of 7.2 days and takes just two days to go from its minimum to its maximum brightness.

NGC 6709

Mag
6.7

On the western edge of the constellation, NGC 6709 is the most easily observed open cluster in Aquila. It covers 12′ and contains around 40 stars.

SCORPIUS

VISIBLE: summer (on Meridian at 21:00 in mid-July)

Scorpius is a very rich constellation, brimming with stellar clusters of all kinds.

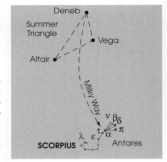

The best way to find Scorpius is to follow the Milky Way. From Cygnus (whose bright Deneb is one of the Summer Triangle of stars), the milky streak of our own Galaxy leads directly to a region full of stars, in the middle of which lies Antares, the red giant that is the brightest star in Scorpius. ▷

μ (Mu) SCORPII

Mag 3.1 & 3.1

This double star is probably a physical binary, since its components have similar proper motions. They are 346″ apart, so the system can be resolved with the naked eye. These stars are 821 light years from our Solar System. The westernmost of the pair is an eclipsing binary star.

M4

Mag 5.9

This is one of the largest (26′) and closest globular clusters (6,800 light years distant). With a magnitude of 5.9 and just over 1° away from α (Alpha) Scorpii (Antares), it is visible to the naked eye on a dark enough night. However, for observers in mid-northern latitudes Scorpius does not rise high above the horizon, which makes it less easy to see. In the smallest pair of binoculars its whitish glow is unmistakable, and with a 4-inch (100 mm) telescope some detail can be seen in its central region, including a bright bar made up of a group of stars almost in a straight line.

M4, one of the brightest globular clusters in the whole sky, can be found right next to Antares. ▷

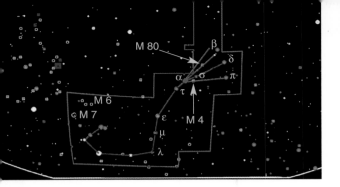

M6 (BUTTERFLY CLUSTER)

This open cluster contains stars of magnitudes 7 to 10 arranged roughly in the shape of a butterfly with open wings. The "wingspan" is 15′, corresponding to a diameter of around 10 light years. Even in the simplest astronomical telescope, this group of stars 1,950 light years distant is a magical sight.

M7

This is another open cluster, and also easy to see with the naked eye. It extends over 1° of sky, contains 60 stars of magnitudes between 6 and 10, and is nearly 800 light years from the Solar System. Binoculars, or a small telescope with a large field, are ideal for observing this cluster.

M62

This globular cluster, lying 7° southeast of α (Alpha) Scorpii, is fairly bright but, due to its position right in the central Galactic hub, its light seems much weaker to us because of the interstellar dust and gases it has to pass through. Without this absorbent veil, it would probably be two magnitudes brighter. The cluster, which extends over 14′ of arc and is 20,000 light years away, retains its cloudlike appearance in most telescopes, looking rather like a comet. Only with the help of a 12-inch (300 mm) telescope does it become possible to distinguish some of the stars individually.

M80

The globular cluster M80 is not difficult to find, since it is exactly on a line between the two brightest stars in Scorpius, α (Alpha) (Antares) and β (Beta) Scorpii. It is 27,000 light years away and 40 light years across, but only extends over 9′ of our sky.

SAGITTARIUS

VISIBLE: summer (on Meridian at 21:00 in mid-August)

Sagittarius, the Archer, is a large constellation in the Zodiac which never rises high in the sky over the northern hemisphere. Within it is the brightest part of the Milky Way.

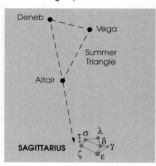

Sagittarius is just east of Scorpius. Take a line from Deneb to Altair, and extend it by the same distance to arrive in the middle of this constellation, just a little to the east of its brightest stars, which resemble a teapot. ▷

THE MILKY WAY

 Mag ind

The Milky Way shines brighter in Sagittarius than anywhere else, for the simple reason that the center of the Galaxy lies in this direction. The whitish trail we see is the combined light from tens of thousands of millions of stars. If the area is swept with binoculars or a low-magnification telescope, many thousands of stars appear in the field of view.

M8 (LAGOON NEBULA)

 Mag 5

This is one of the two great nebulae visible to the naked eye from the northern hemisphere, the other being the Orion Nebula. In a small telescope, it shows as a pale patch around an open cluster (NGC 6530). A band of dark dust, dividing it in two, can be seen with an 8 or 10-inch

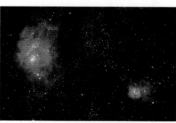

(200 or 250 mm) telescope. This most beautiful nebula, some 5,000 light years away, contains many stars in the process of formation.

◁ *The Lagoon (left) and Trifid Nebulae: two beautiful nebulae not far apart in the sky.*

M20 (TRIFID NEBULA)

 Mag 6.3

A little over 1° north of M8 is another very lovely nebula: M20. It extends over 25′ of arc, and its brightest area is split into three by a dark structure that can be seen with an 8-inch (200 mm) telescope if viewing conditions are very good. Just next to it lies the open cluster M21.

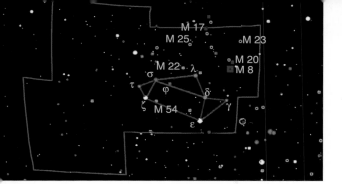

M17 (OMEGA or HORSESHOE NEBULA)

Mag 6

Yet another famous nebula in Sagittarius! Almost at the border with the constellation Scutum, this gaseous cloud has a shape more like the figure 2 than the Ω (Omega) that William Herschel saw in it. In an amateur instrument, M17 looks rather like an elongated comet. It is about 5,000 light years away and extends over more than 40′ of arc.

M22

Mag 5.1

This is one of the finest globular clusters in the whole of the heavens. In the northern skies, only M13 in Hercules is brighter. M22 is one of the nearest globular clusters to the Solar System, only 10,000 light years distant. Many hundreds of its stars can be seen in an 8-inch (200 mm) telescope.

M23

Mag 5.5

This open cluster can be observed with binoculars; it is 2,150 light years from the Solar System.

M25

Mag 4.6

Another easy open cluster for amateurs to observe; it is about 1,900 light years away, and 20 light years across.

M54

Mag 7.7

A fairly bright globular cluster, and quite compact (covering only 9′). It is 70,000 light years away, and not easy to resolve into stars with a telescope less than 10 inches (250 mm) in aperture. With a smaller instrument, though, it can easily be seen as a cloudy disk.

CAPRICORNUS

VISIBLE: summer (on Meridian at 21:00 in mid-September)

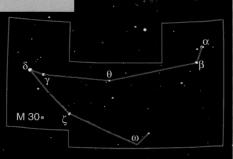

This constellation can be seen at the end of summer, but never rises far above the horizon, particularly for those in higher northern latitudes. Though fairly extensive, it has few objects of much interest to amateur astronomers.

△ *Capricornus can be found quite far to the south of the small, but distinctive, constellation Delphinus. A line from Alpheratz to Markab (in the Great Square of Pegasus) points toward Capricornus.*

α (Alpha) CAPRICORNI (ALGEDI)

Mag 3.5 & 4

This is an optical double (there is no gravitational connection between the two stars) which can be resolved with the naked eye, like Mizar and Alcor in Ursa Major: the separation between the two is 376″.

β (Beta) CAPRICORNI

Mag 3 & 6

This optical double is fairly easy to resolve with any small astronomical telescope. The stars are 344 and 850 light years away.

M30

Mag 7

This magnitude 7 globular cluster, 27,000 light years away, can easily be observed with a small telescope. However, in the higher northern latitudes it stays too close to the horizon, where there is often mist or light pollution, to be easy to locate. It is just 20′ from 41 Capricorni, a star of magnitude 5.3.

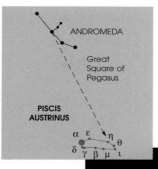

The Southern Fish is a constellation of the southern hemisphere which never rises high for those in the north, and is often completely hidden from higher northern latitudes. The rectangular constellation contains a number of double stars.

△ *A line from γ (Almach) to β (Mirach) Andromedae gives the direction of Piscis Austrinus, though it is quite far away, and only its brightest star, α (Alpha) Piscis Austrini, makes it relatively easy to find.*

β (Beta) PISCIS AUSTRINI

Mag 4.5 & 7.5

The second brightest star in the constellation, and a good example of an optical double. Separated by over 30″, the two stars can be distinguished in any astronomical instrument.

LACAILLE 9352

Mag 7.4

This star, in the southeast corner of the constellation and 1° south of π (Pi) Piscis Austrini, is notable for its very large proper motion: it is in fact the fourth fastest-moving star in the whole sky, moving 6.9″ of arc every year. With a good telescope, then, it is possible to observe its movement against the background of the distant stars over the course of a few years. It is only 10.7 light years away.

γ (Gamma) PISCIS AUSTRINI

Mag 4.5 & 8

Another double star, with components 4.2″ apart. They are separable with a 2-inch (50 mm) telescope, but the magnitude difference makes it difficult.

AQUARIUS

VISIBLE: fall (on Meridian at 21:00 in early October)

This constellation is located on the ecliptic, and contains a number of objects well worth studying.

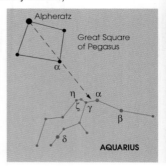

Aquarius has no very bright stars, and its pattern is not one of the easiest to make out. However, it is not difficult to locate: take a line joining Alpheratz to α (Alpha) Pegasi in the Great Square of Pegasus, and extend it for the same distance again to reach two of Aquarius's brighter stars, α (Alpha) and γ (Gamma) Aquarii. ▷

ζ (Zeta) AQUARII

Mag 4.3 & 4.5

This is a physical binary whose components are only 2.1″ apart. It takes 850 years for one star to complete its orbit around the other. The pair makes a good test of vision for observers with instruments around 2 inches (50 mm) in diameter.

M2

Mag 6.5

This is a globular cluster on the very northern edge of the constellation. It can be observed with the smallest of telescopes, but because of its distance (37,000 light years) an 8-inch (200 mm) instrument is necessary to see any of its individual stars. Its apparent diameter, 12′, represents an actual size of over 100 light years across.

NGC 7009 (SATURN NEBULA)

Mag 8

This planetary nebula is very well known among astronomers, and can be observed with amateur equipment. However, although it is relatively bright, it looks rather disappointing, since the central region is only 25″ across, making it really quite a small object. The structure of the nebula, which looks a little like the planet Saturn with its rings, only begins to

The Saturn Nebula ▷

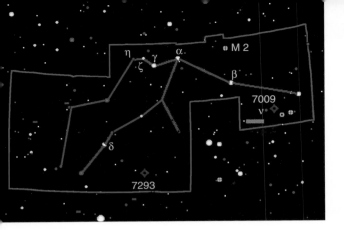

emerge when viewed with a telescope at least 10 inches (250 mm) in diameter. To find this nebula, start at ν (Nu) Aquarii, a magnitude 4.5 star, and look 1° 18′ to the west. It is a shell of expanding gases, 0.5 light years across, that has been thrown off by a central star of magnitude 11.5.

A little under 3° to the west of NGC 7009 is a globular cluster, M72, one of the least dense we know. It is 85 light years across, 56,000 light years away, and not easy to resolve into stars.

NGC 7293 (HELIX NEBULA)

Mag 8

This is the closest and largest planetary nebula of all. It is only 450 light years away from the Solar System, and its apparent diameter is about half that of the Moon's disk. Nevertheless, the Helix is not always an easy object to observe, for it does not give off a great deal of light. Finding it therefore requires some dedication. It is 1.75 light years across, and in binoculars it looks like a pale smoke ring. Those with small telescopes should set them to the lowest possible magnification in order to find the nebula. With a powerful enough instrument, the central star can be seen; it is a magnitude 13.5 white dwarf.

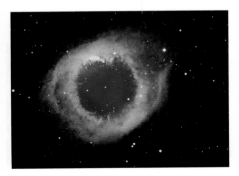

◁ The Helix Nebula, closest of all the planetary nebulae.

SCULPTOR

VISIBLE: fall (on Meridian at 21:00 in early November)

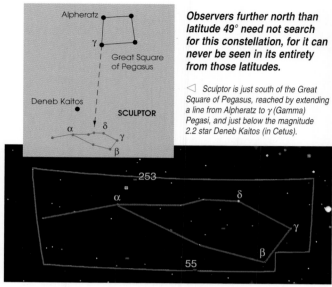

Observers further north than latitude 49° need not search for this constellation, for it can never be seen in its entirety from those latitudes.

◁ *Sculptor is just south of the Great Square of Pegasus, reached by extending a line from Alpheratz to γ (Gamma) Pegasi, and just below the magnitude 2.2 star Deneb Kaitos (in Cetus).*

NGC 55

Mag 8

This galaxy is one of our closest neighbors, after M31 and M33, and other members of the Local Group; it is 6 million light years away. It is of the irregular type and extends over 20′, as a whitish bar.

NGC 253

Mag 7

This superb spiral galaxy (7° 30′ to the south of Deneb Kaitos) is the brightest in the Sculptor group, which also includes NGC 55. It shows what the Milky Way would look like, if seen from a point outside and slightly above its equatorial plane. This galaxy is 7.8 million light years away and extends over 25′ of arc; it can be observed with binoculars, and details begin to be visible in the central region with the aid of an 8 to 10-inch (200 to 250 mm) telescope.

◁ *NGC 253: a splendid galaxy, but not easy to observe from higher northern latitudes.*

Visible: fall (on Meridian at 21:00 in mid-December)

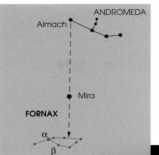

Like all the southern constellations, Fornax barely rises above the horizon for observers in the northern hemisphere. Only those below 45° will be able to study it.

Fornax is not easy to find, as it lies in a region of the sky with few bright stars. One method is to take a line from γ (Gamma) Andromedae (Almach) to Mira (in Cetus) and extend it southwards: the constellation begins 20° south of Mira.

α (Alpha) FORNACIS

Mag 4 & 6.5

The companion star that revolves around α (Alpha) Fornacis is at an average angular distance of 3.2″ and takes no less than 300 years to complete one orbit. This physical binary system is 40 light years away from Earth.

NGC 1316

Mag 8

This magnitude 9 spiral galaxy, over 80 million light years away, can be observed by amateur astronomers with telescopes as small as 2½ inches (60 mm) in diameter.

NGC 1398

Mag 10

Another spiral galaxy, not so bright but easier for those in the northern hemisphere to observe, since it rises higher above the horizon.

CAELUM

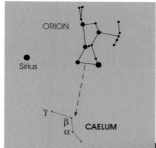

Caelum, The Chisel, is a tiny constellation created in 1752. It is only visible from lower northern latitudes in late fall and winter, and it does not rise far above the horizon, making observation difficult. It has very few objects of interest.

△ It is not easy to find this constellation, which has no bright stars: it lies far (30°) to the south of Orion and southwest of Sirius.

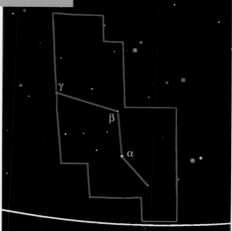

α (Alpha) CAELI

Mag 4.5 & 13

The brightest star in Caelum is actually a double, estimated to be 65 light years away. But a 6-inch (150 mm) telescope is needed to see both components, as the second star, 8.6″ away from the principal one, is only of magnitude 12.5.

γ (Gamma) CAELI

Mag 4.5 & 8

The two stars which make up this binary system, 170 light years distant, are only separated by 2.9″ of arc. However, they are bright enough to be visible with any amateur equipment.

VISIBLE: winter (on Meridian at 21:00 in early February)

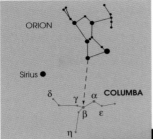

For observers above 46° north, this constellation always remains partially hidden by the horizon. It contains few interesting objects, apart from one optical double and one globular cluster.

△ *Columba (The Dove) is directly below Orion and to the southwest of Canis Major, whose principal star, Sirius, is the brightest star in the sky.*

α (Alpha) COLUMBAE (PHACT)

Mag 3 & 11

The brightest star in Columba, 140 light years from our Solar System, has a magnitude 11 companion at a distance of 15.5″ of arc. However, the two stars are only apparent neighbors, for they have very different proper motions, and the gap between them has been increasing steadily since 1900.

μ (Mu) COLUMBAE

Mag 5.2

This star's high velocity indicates that it has been ejected from its original location in the constellation Orion, perhaps by a supernova explosion.

NGC 1851

Mag 7.3

This globular cluster, 35,000 light years away, makes a good target for amateurs with small telescopes who are sufficiently far south for it not to be lost in the mists near the horizon.

PYXIS

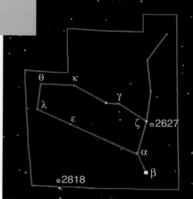

Pyxis, the Compass, was named by Lacaille in 1752. It is a southerly constellation of no great interest to amateur observers, although it does have some quite close doubles and some open clusters.

△ *This constellation may be named after a navigational instrument, but that does not make it easy to find! Take a line from Rigel to Saiph in Orion, and extend it to the east by six times its length to arrive at the two principal stars in Pyxis.*

ε (Epsilon) PYXIDIS

Mag 5.5 & 9.5

The instruments available to amateurs can only reveal two of this star system's three components, 17.8″ apart. The third is only 0.3″ from the principal star, and outshone by its light.

NGC 2627

Mag 8.4

An open cluster, 8,200 light years away and easy to find, just to the west of ζ (Zeta) Pyxidis.

NGC 2818

Mag 8.2

This open cluster is 10,400 light years away. In the same field of view is NGC 2818A, an irregularly shaped planetary nebula of magnitude 13, very difficult to see with amateur equipment.

Visible: spring (on Meridian at 21:00 in early April)

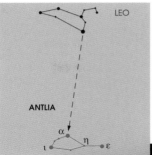

A constellation of southern latitudes which hardly rises above the horizon in Europe or the northern USA: above 48° it can never be seen in its entirety, and it remains hidden from observers in Scandinavia and Canada.

△ *Antlia (the Air Pump) lies approximately south of Leo, about 45° distant.*

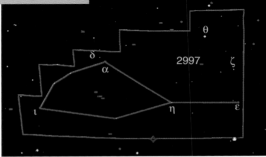

ζ (Zeta) ANTLIAE

Mag 5.8 & 5.9

The western, slightly brighter member of this wide pair has a companion of magnitude 7 at an angular distance of 8.2″.

NGC 2997

Mag 11

This is a spiral galaxy, but very difficult to find because it is faint and, viewed from northern latitudes, always very low over the horizon. It lies

3° to the east of ζ (Zeta) Antliae. It has an apparent diameter of about 7′, and lies at a distance of some 40 million light years.

◁ *NGC 2997 is a "cousin" of the Milky Way. We view its spiral arms full on.*

PUPPIS

The constellation Puppis (the Poop Deck or Stern of a ship) is never visible in its entirety for observers in mid-northern latitudes. It has some interesting open clusters, but they lie so close to the horizon that they are rather difficult to study.

Puppis is not difficult to find. It lies southeast of Canis Major, which is unmistakable because it contains Sirius, the brightest star in the sky. ▷

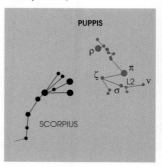

π (Pi) PUPPIS

Mag
2.7, 4.7 & 5.1

Located 25′ northeast of π (Pi) Puppis are two stars of roughly the same brightness, 4′ apart. These have a bluish hue and make a striking contrast with the orange of the giant π (Pi) Puppis itself. The two blue stars may form a physical binary, though it has not so far been possible to confirm this by observation.

L² PUPPIS

Mag
3.1 & 5.8

This star, in the southernmost part of the constellation, is a red variable and one of the brightest known. Its variability was detected in 1872, and its brightness varies over a period of 141 days. L² also forms an optical double with another star, of magnitude 9.5, which is just 1′ of arc away. Because it can be very close to the horizon, this is not an easy star to observe, except from fairly low northern latitudes. It cannot be seen at all by observers above 40° north.

M47

Mag
4.4

This bright open cluster can be found by taking a line from β (Beta) Canis Majoris to Sirius and extending it over a distance of 12°33′. The cluster can be observed with binoculars. It is around 1,600 light years distant and 17 light years across.

M46

Mag
6.1

Lying 1°21′ east of M47, this is another open cluster, not so bright but extremely interesting. M46 in fact contains a planetary nebula, NGC 2438, which looks as if it belongs to the cluster. However, measurements have shown that NGC 2438 is closer: it lies in the foreground, 2,900 light years

away, while M46 is 5,400 light years distant. The planetary nebula, with an apparent diameter of 1.3′, is of magnitude 10, so it is not an easy object to observe.

On the other hand, M46, together with NGC 2438 and M47, lies in the northern part of the constellation, so all of these objects can easily be seen by observers in mid-northern latitudes (around 45°).

M46 and the planetary nebula NGC 2438, which is not in fact part of the cluster, but situated well in front of it. ▷

M93

Mag 6.2

Another fine open cluster, extending over 22.4′ and a good target for amateur observers. It is 3,600 light years away and has some 80 stars.

NGC 2477

Mag 5.8

Under the best conditions, this cluster can be seen with the naked eye. However, this is not often possible in mid-northern latitudes, since it remains very close to the horizon. At 4,200 light years, it is more distant than M46 and contains some 160 stars, spread over 27′ of arc.

NORMA

SMALL**Visible:** summer (on Meridian at 21:00 in early July)

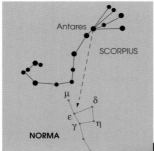

This little constellation marks the southerly limit of what can be seen from the mid-northern latitudes. In North America, only observers south of Memphis or Oklahoma can see it; In Europe, only those in the extreme south (near Gibraltar).

△ Norma (the Level) lies 15° south of Antares in the constellation Scorpius.

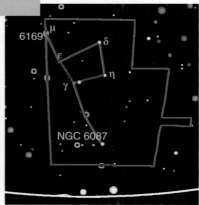

δ (Delta) NORMAE

Mag 4.8

This single star is the northernmost of the brighter stars in the constellation Norma.

ε (Epsilon) NORMAE

Mag 4.5 & 7.5

The two components of this binary are very difficult to distinguish, even from lower latitudes. They are 22″ apart and form a true physical binary, around 500 light years from Earth.

NGC 6087

Mag 5.4

This open cluster, in the southeast of the constellation, is the brightest in this part of the sky. It extends over 12′ and contains around 40 stars.

VISIBLE: summer (on Meridian at 21:00 in mid-August)

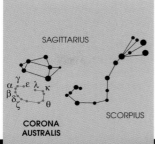

SAGITTARIUS

γ
α ε λ κ
β δ ζ θ

CORONA AUSTRALIS

SCORPIUS

This constellation cannot be observed by those above 50° north, but in any case it has little of interest for amateurs: just one globular cluster and one triple star.

◁ *Corona Australis lies just south of Sagittarius and east of the tail of Scorpius.*

α γ ε
β λ κ
δ
ζ θ

6541

λ (Lambda) CORONAE AUSTRALIS

Mag 5, 9 & 10

This triple system is 170 light years from Earth and the component stars are separated by 29″ and 40″. It lies in the northern part of the constellation, and is relatively easy to find for those below 40° north with an uncluttered horizon.

NGC 6541

Mag 6.6

A globular cluster 22,000 light years away, extending over 13′. It lies in the southwest corner of the constellation, not far from the Scorpion's tail.

MICROSCOPIUM

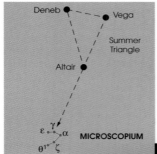

In the northern hemisphere, only those in middle or low latitudes will be able to see this constellation: it does not rise fully above the horizon for those above 42° north. Its main interest is the double stars it contains.

△ *To find the Microscope, use the Summer Triangle, extending the line from Vega to Altair.*

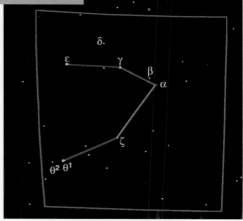

α (Alpha) MICROSCOPII

Mag 5 & 9.5

This, the principal star in Microscopium, has a companion 20.6″ away. These two bodies are about 240 light years from the Sun.

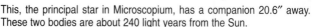

θ² (Theta²) MICROSCOPII

Mag 6.5 & 7

This double star is not easy to resolve: the angular separation is less than 0.5″. You will need a telescope with an aperture of at least 12 inches (300 mm), and minimal air turbulence, which is rarely found when the constellation is low above the horizon.

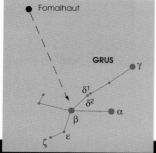

GRUS

Visible: fall (on Meridian at 21:00 in early October)

One of the southernmost constellations visible: even at the latitude of Memphis or Gibraltar, not all of it rises above the horizon.

◁ *A line from β (Beta) to α (Alpha) Pegasi, extended to the south by about three times its length, leads to α (Alpha) Piscis Austrinus (Fomalhaut); one more length takes you to β (Beta) Gruis.*

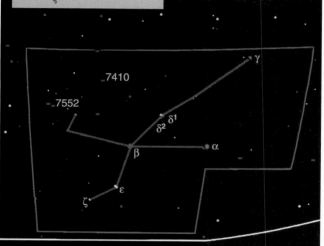

NGC 7552

Mag 11

NGC 7552 is a barred spiral galaxy, but it is not very bright and is difficult to see. A trip to the tropics or the southern hemisphere would probably offer the best opportunity to observe this object under reasonable conditions.

NGC 7410

Mag 10

The same applies to this galaxy, which is located almost as far south as the last.

PHENOMENA OF THE NIGHT SKY

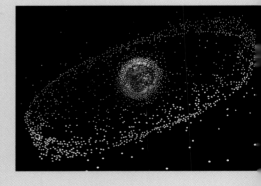

ZODIACAL LIGHT AND POLAR AURORAS

Polar auroras and the zodiacal light are both luminous phenomena that can be seen with the naked eye. They have nothing else in common, and their causes are completely different.

THE ZODIACAL LIGHT

Description

This bright glow in the western sky after sunset, or in the eastern sky before sunrise, is due to the existence of a tenuous disk of dust around the Sun. The disk has a radius of 600 million kilometers and reaches almost as far out as the orbit of Jupiter. However, only its inner part is dense enough to diffuse sunlight falling on it, making it visible just after dusk or just before dawn. The zodiacal halo is roughly elliptical

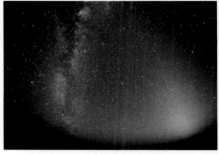

△ Zodiacal light and the Milky Way

and aligned with the ecliptic. The dust that causes this phenomenon has been left behind in the region of the Sun by the countless comets that have passed through the inner Solar System over thousands of millions of years.

Observing the zodiacal light

It is not easy to see the zodiacal light, and you need to choose your moment well. Because the glow extends along the plane of the ecliptic, the best view is obtained when this is perpendicular to the horizon. The angle depends on the season, and it follows that September and October are the best months to see the zodiacal light in the east (morning), while February and March are best for viewing it in the west (evening). A moonless night and a site well away from artificial lighting are both essential.

POLAR AURORAS

Description

Auroras usually occur only in high latitudes, creating immense sheets of bright light in the sky. They are the result of interaction between the upper layers of the Earth's atmosphere and the particles that stream from the Sun, especially after solar flares. These electrically charged particles are trapped in the Earth's magnetic field and pass through the gases of the upper atmosphere at very high speed. The encounter, between 80 and

△ *A polar aurora*

200 kilometers up, produces a glow which can easily be seen from the ground. Astronauts orbiting at around 400 kilometers above the Earth can view this spectacle from above, a privileged vantage point. Polar auroras seen in the northern hemisphere are known as northern lights (aurora borealis) and those in the southern hemisphere as southern lights (aurora australis).

Observing polar auroras

Because the particles that cause the aurora follow the lines of the Earth's magnetic field, which concentrate at the poles, the ideal place for observing these sheets of light is bound to be near the poles. In Europe, northern Scandinavia and Iceland offer the best locations. Auroras can occur at any time, but are most likely during periods of great solar activity. When this is particularly intense, the phenomenon can exceptionally be observed at lower latitudes.

△ *An aurora seen from above, by astronauts on a US Space Shuttle.*

METEORS

DESCRIPTION

As it travels round the Solar System, the Earth is constantly crossing the paths of millions of pieces of cosmic debris: particles of dust and small rocks. Entering Earth's atmosphere at great speed, they burn up and produce what are called "falling stars," "shooting stars," or "meteors." The cause is most often a small grain the size of a pea, igniting at a height of around 100 kilometers and leaving a bright trail which lasts only a fraction of a second. Unless you are looking in exactly the right direction, you will only see a tiny flash of light. About 100 tons of dust arrive in our atmosphere in this way every day.

Comets are the source of this debris. Every time they approach the Sun, they release gas, a process known as "outgassing:" in the heat of the Sun, some of their ice turns to gas and disperses in space, freeing dust and small particles as it does so. It is these residues that become meteors.

Once loose in space, the cometary debris follows its own trajectory, which is why meteors can be seen at any time of the year. Most of the particles, though, continue along the orbit of their parent comet, and the Earth, as it travels in its own path round the Sun, crosses each of these orbital paths at the same time every year. In some cases the comet still exists and in others it has long since disappeared, but as Earth reaches the intersection zone it enters what is called a "meteor stream." For a day or more, depending on the width of the stream, the number of meteors is much greater than normal: during such "showers" it is not unusual to see a dozen in just half an hour.

Some orbiting debris, originating in collisions between asteroids, consists of larger stones ranging in size from pebbles to rocks several meters across. These do not always burn up in the atmosphere, but may fall to Earth, and are then known as meteorites. Although they are rarely seen falling, fallen ones can be found on the ground.

This meteor was captured in a long-exposure photograph. ▷

HISTORY AND DISCOVERIES

The observation of meteors must go back to the very dawn of the human race, since anyone who looks up at the sky is bound to see one sooner or later, even without looking out for them. In ancient times these short-lived brilliant streaks were thought to be exhalations of the Earth itself. Aristotle (384–322 B.C.) suggested that such exhalations occurred where the terrestrial world met the "aether," the divine material of the upper sphere where the stars were to be found. For a long time, this view was accepted. Then hypotheses were put forward suggesting that electricity was involved, and that meteors might be related to lightning. Eventually, the German physicist Ernst Chladni (1756–1827) discovered the extraterrestrial origin of meteors and meteorites, but it took another 25 years for his ideas to become accepted.

OBSERVING METEORS

The best equipment for observing meteors is definitely a settee or a mattress. A comfortable vantage point is not a luxury, but essential, especially for long periods of observation. Then all you need to do is watch the skies – and wait. Meteors can occur in any part of the sky, and are statistically twice as likely at the end of the night as at the beginning, because in the morning an observer is "in front" of the Earth as it moves through space. Just as more rain hits the front windshield of a car than the rear, so the Earth encounters meteors mostly in the direction of its motion. During a meteor shower, though, the time of night hardly matters: it is difficult to miss them.

Each regular shower of meteors appears to come from the direction of one particular constellation, and this constellation gives its name to the shower. This does not mean that they in fact originate in the stars of that constellation, merely that they appear to radiate from that particular point in the sky, which is known as the radiant.

PRINCIPAL METEOR SHOWERS

Period	Name	Radiant
1–4 January	Quadrantids	Boötes
12–24 April	Lyrids	Lyra
1–13 May	Eta Aquarids	Aquarius
25–30 July	Delta Aquarids	Aquarius
9–14 August	Perseids	Perseus
8–10 October	Draconids	Draco
11–30 October	Orionids	Orion
14–22 November	Leonids	Leo
5–19 December	Geminids	Gemini

The dates are more or less the same every year.

ARTIFICIAL SATELLITES

DESCRIPTION

When watching the night sky with the naked eye, it is not unusual these days to see small bright dots that move. Some of them may be airplanes, which can be recognized by their winking navigation lights, but artificial satellites are also becoming more and more common, crisscrossing the starry background above the Earth's atmosphere. Most of them are covered with highly reflective aluminum thermal shielding, which makes them easily visible, even when they are over 300 kilometers above our heads. The ones that are visible to the naked eye are those in relatively low orbits, which means somewhere between 250 and 500 kilometers up: they are generally about the size of an automobile, and can be seen without instruments.

Traveling at 28,000 kilometers per hour, artificial satellites take around three minutes to cross the whole sky, but quite often disappear before they reach the far horizon, as they move into the Earth's shadow. They are visible only because they are lit by the Sun against the dark sky, and when they pass out of the sunlight they disappear completely from view. Some of these satellites can be extremely bright, even brighter than Venus: these are the larger spacecraft, such as the US Space Shuttles or the International Space Station (ISS).

HISTORY

The first ever sighting of an artificial satellite was in October 1957, when Sputnik 1, the first such satellite to orbit the Earth, was launched. The Soviet leaders were keen to advertise their technical prowess to the Western world, and published its coordinates and transit times for many countries, so that the "beep" of its radio beacon could be detected there. During those days of October 1957, many amateur astronomers and interested observers saw Sputnik 1 passing overhead. Since then, a number of

◁ Every year there are more satellite launches: here, an Ariane 4 rocket blasts off. There are now whole clusters of communications satellites, each one a bright, new artificial star in the night sky – not at all a good thing for astronomy.

◁ On wide-field photographs with long exposures, such as this telescopic view of a nebula, it is increasingly common for an artificial satellite to leave its mark: a long, bright trail. The traffic is getting heavier!

More and more manufactured objects are orbiting the Earth; in fact, some orbits are becoming crowded. A ring is beginning to form at 36,000 kilometers up. ▷

organizations in the USA, the UK, and elsewhere have been set up to track the thousands of satellites and pieces of space debris in orbit around the Earth. In fact, it has become necessary keep them under observation, in order to avoid collisions with the manned spaceships that are regularly being launched.

OBSERVING SATELLITES

There are two ways of locating artificial satellites: by chance, and by referring to forecasts. Actually, the first method is not at all difficult: just by watching for a few minutes, you will have a good chance of seeing one, since so many of these devices have been sent into space. Those that appear to move from west to east are on orbits at a slight angle to the equator, while those that seem to follow lines of longitude are following polar orbits.

If you want to watch a particular satellite, you will need to know its coordinates and transit times. The International Space Station, for example, passes over North America and Europe – but you have to know when. The best time for both chance and planned observation is two or three hours after sunset in the evening, or a similar time before sunrise in the morning. This is because artificial satellites must be in sunlight to be visible. If they pass overhead late at night, they move more swiftly into the Earth's cone of shadow and disappear from sight.

Detailed information about how to locate and observe artificial satellites can be found on the Internet. Try, for example, the NASA site. There are also other useful sites giving the transit times of hundreds of satellites.

CONJUNCTIONS AND OCCULTATIONS

DESCRIPTION

Now and then, in their unending journeys around the Sun, the planets move in front of stars or nebulae. At such times it is possible to observe a body belonging to the Solar System in the same field of view as a stellar cluster thousands of light years away, and we say that the two bodies are in conjunction. Very close conjunction occurs when the two objects can be seen at the same time in a telescope, but more frequently they are a few degrees apart and can be observed together only with the naked eye. On occasion, three or even four objects can appear side by side.

Astronomers dream of wonderful conjunctions between the planets and Messier or NGC objects (nebulae or galaxies), but not every combination is possible. For example, no planet could ever pass in front of the Orion Nebula (M42) or the Andromeda Galaxy (M31), for the very good reason that these objects lie far from the ecliptic. As the seasons pass, the planets revolve within a band that extends just a few degrees either side of the ecliptic, and only objects within this band can be "approached" by a planet. The list of such nebulae and galaxies is not a long one: they all necessarily belong to constellations in the Zodiac (with the addition of Ophiuchus, which also straddles the ecliptic). The best known candidates for conjunctions with planets are the Pleiades and the Hyades (in Taurus), the Praesepe or Beehive Cluster (in Cancer), the Lagoon and Trifid Nebulae (in Sagittarius), and the open cluster M35 (in Gemini). In Virgo, the elliptical galaxy NGC 4697, though less well known, lies precisely on the ecliptic.

The Moon is also involved in this game of hide-and-seek, and it can happen – though rarely – that the Moon occults one of the planets. Even the amateur observer with a small astronomical instrument can then watch at leisure, as the planet takes a few tens of seconds to disappear

△ *This photograph was taken on September 12, 1983, as Jupiter and the Moon came close in the sky.*

234

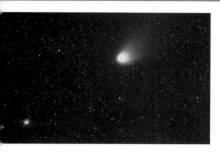

◁ *A very rare encounter: Comet Hale–Bopp passes close to the globular cluster M14.*

behind the edge of the Moon (this is known as immersion) and then reappears on the other side an hour later (called emersion). On extremely rare occasions, a planet may occult quite a bright star. A "grazing occultation" of a star by the Moon is an extraordinary event, for then the star may wink more than once as it passes behind the mountains on the Moon's rim. Even amateur astronomers can observe this phenomenon.

Conjunctions between comets and other heavenly objects can be spectacular sights. Since a comet's orbit does not necessarily lie close to the plane of the ecliptic, it may come into conjunction with any object in the sky. For example, Comet Hale–Bopp passed close by the globular cluster M14 in 1997. But events like this only happen once in a lifetime.

HISTORY AND DISCOVERIES

Conjunctions between planets and stars have been observed since very early times. The history of this phenomenon is quickly told: as soon as astronomers were able to understand and model the movements of bodies in the Solar System, it became possible to predict their conjunctions with some precision.

OBSERVING THESE PHENOMENA

Specialist magazines and almanacs give details of any conjunctions and occultations that are about to occur. The Moon passes close to other bodies every month, and most of these conjunctions can be observed with the naked eye; but to get a good view of an occultation, a telescope is needed.

A conjunction of Venus, Mars, Jupiter, and the Moon, visible with the naked eye. ▷

235

SOLAR ECLIPSES

DESCRIPTION

When the Moon passes exactly between the Earth and the Sun, it hides the Sun from part of the Earth's surface: this is an eclipse of the Sun. It is something that can only happen at new moon, but not every new moon brings an eclipse, since most of the time the Moon passes slightly above or below the exact line between Sun and Earth. In fact, solar eclipses occur only twice a year.

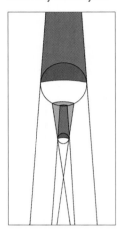

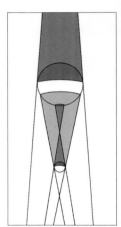

◁ *During a total eclipse of the Sun, the Moon casts its full shadow (umbra) onto the Earth, masking the Sun completely.*

During an annular eclipse, the Moon's umbra does not reach the Earth. ▷

Unlike lunar eclipses, which can be seen by all observers on the "night" hemisphere of the Earth, a solar eclipse can only be seen from part of the Earth's "day" side. The full shadow (umbra) cast by the Moon on the Earth is a moving circle, at most 270 kilometers in diameter. Thus, during a total eclipse, the Sun is not completely hidden for observers outside this "path of totality." (The 1999 solar eclipse visible from eastern Canada to Calcutta covered a band only 100 kilometers wide.) Outside this band, but within a wider area which may be up to 3,000 kilometers across, only a partial eclipse is seen. Elsewhere, the eclipse is not visible at all.

The distance between the Earth and the Moon varies from 350,000 to 400,000 kilometers. When the Moon is at its furthest from the Earth, its apparent size in the sky is too small to hide the Sun entirely. Its full shadow does not reach the Earth's surface, and the result is an annular eclipse: a ring or "annulus" of Sun is still visible all round the Moon, even at the eclipse's maximum.

HISTORY AND DISCOVERIES

Ancient astronomers tried to find out whether solar eclipses occurred in a regular cyclical pattern: the Mesopotamians (around 700 B.C.) and the Maya (around 500 B.C.) both discovered that a similar eclipse recurs

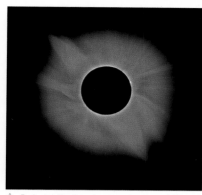

△ *During totality, the solar corona becomes visible.*

every 54 years. This period is in fact equal to three times the actual cycle in which a particular configuration occurs, which is 18 years and 11 days (a "saros"). However, the exact period does not correspond to a whole number of days, so although an eclipse does take place every 18 years, the rotation of the Earth means that each eclipse is seen from a part of the Earth's surface 120° of longitude away from the previous one. Observers in ancient times would only witness one in three of these events, hence their calculation of a 54-year cycle. In modern times, astronomers have used solar eclipses as opportunities to study the solar corona, though nowadays they do not need to wait for an eclipse, because they can occult the Sun artificially by means of a coronograph, an instrument invented by the French astronomer Bernard Lyot.

OBSERVING SOLAR ECLIPSES

The same precautions are necessary when observing a solar eclipse as when observing the Sun itself (see p.84): otherwise, there is a danger of sight loss. The whole phenomenon takes several hours from start to finish, and may be observed through special Mylar spectacles, a pair of binoculars with Mylar shades, or a small telescope with a solar filter using only low magnification. The period of totality lasts no more than eight minutes, during which the sky turns almost as dark as night and the brighter stars appear, together with any planets that happen to be above the horizon. This is an excellent time for locating Mercury, normally so hard to see. The solar corona is clearly visible, even with the unaided eye. If you watch the eclipse from a high vantage point, such as a hilltop above a plain, you will see the full shadow of the Moon rushing across the ground toward you and then receding again.

For observers of a partial eclipse, it remains daylight, as enough of the Sun is still visible. ▷

237

LUNAR ECLIPSES

DESCRIPTION

When the Moon passes through the Earth's shadow, a lunar eclipse takes place: so, for an eclipse to happen, Moon, Earth, and Sun must be in a straight line. Put like this, it sounds as if an eclipse might be expected every month, at each full moon, but this is not so: there are only two or three eclipses in a year. This is because the Moon's orbit is at a slight angle to the plane of the ecliptic. Most times, at the precise moment of full moon, the Moon is passing above or below the shadow of the Earth. For the same reason, not all lunar eclipses are full eclipses: the Moon does not always pass entirely within the circular shadow of the Earth, and when it does not, only part of the Moon is obscured. A crescent still lit by the Sun remains visible. Finally, there are penumbral eclipses, where the Moon does not pass through the Earth's full shadow (the umbra), but only through its partial shadow (the penumbra). Some, but not all, of the Sun's rays penetrate this penumbra, so that the dimming of the Moon is very slight, and not at all easy to see. Even during a

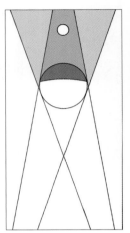

△ *A lunar eclipse occurs every time the Moon passes within the cone of shadow cast by the Earth; this is always at full moon.*

total eclipse, when the Moon is entirely within the cone of the Earth's umbra, it never disappears altogether: it can be seen as a brighter or deeper shade of red. This is because the atmosphere around the Earth diffracts some of the Sun's rays (especially the red wavelengths) to within the cone of shadow, and it is these rays that are reflected from the Moon, giving it a red color. If there were astronauts on the Moon at the instant of a lunar eclipse, they would see the Sun disappear behind the Earth, and the Earth surrounded by a ring of red light.

HISTORY AND DISCOVERIES

Like solar eclipses, lunar eclipses have been observed since prehistoric times. But those who understood their cause and could predict them sometimes had the upper hand. On his fourth voyage to the New World, Christopher Columbus took with him an early printed copy of an almanac, the *Kalendar* published by the astronomer Regiomontanus. Finding himself in Jamaica and short of supplies, Columbus know there would be an eclipse of the Moon on February 29, 1504. The local inhabitants were convinced that Columbus's prayers had brought the Moon back from oblivion, and gave him and his crew all the food they needed.

△ *A total eclipse of the Moon*

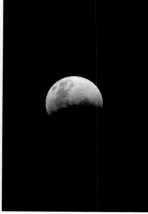

△ *A partial eclipse of the Moon*

OBSERVING LUNAR ECLIPSES

Lunar eclipses are fairly leisurely events, and can easily be followed with a pair of binoculars. A total eclipse may last over 6 hours in all, from beginning to end, but the Moon is usually totally eclipsed for only an hour to an hour and a half.

The best way to watch an eclipse is with binoculars or a low-magnification telescope, so that the whole Moon can be brought within the instrument's field of view. These events can be observed anywhere, even in a city center with all its light pollution. In the country, though, as the Moon darkens during totality, even quite faint objects can be seen, though they would not normally be visible during full moon.

A lunar eclipse can therefore also be a good opportunity to observe faint objects, such as nebulae or galaxies.

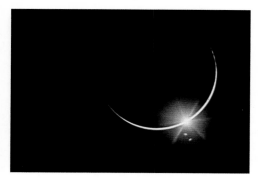

◁ *Seen from the Moon during a lunar eclipse, the Sun is hidden behind the Earth, while the Earth is ringed with a reddish light.*

DESCRIPTION

Mercury and Venus are inferior planets: this means that they move in orbits closer to the Sun than the Earth's. Like the other planets, they revolve in a plane close to the ecliptic. As a result, at regular intervals, one or other of them is exactly aligned between Earth and Sun.

In other words, as seen from Earth, they pass in front of the Sun. As they do so, they do not eclipse the Sun, even though both planets are much larger than the Moon: they are so far away that their apparent diameter is very small, and they hide only a tiny part of the Sun's disk.

These events occur only very rarely, but more often in Mercury's case than that of Venus, since Mercury has the shorter period of revolution. The last transits of Mercury took place in 1999 and on May 7, 2003. Transits of Venus come in pairs eight years apart, with 105 years between pairs. The last transit was on June 8, 2004, and the next one will be eight years later (in 2012). There will then be another long gap before the following transit of Venus.

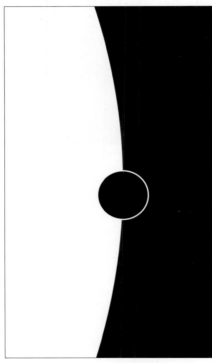

△ *The illumination of Venus's atmosphere as the planet begins its transit.*

HISTORY AND DISCOVERIES

The discovery that Mercury and Venus could on occasion pass in front of the Sun followed the overthrow of the Ptolemaic system, dating from ancient times, according to which all the heavenly bodies revolved around the Earth. After Copernicus had published his model of the Solar System, the astronomer Johannes Kepler studied the planets' movements around the Sun. At first he believed that they moved in circular orbits, but he later discovered that in fact their orbits are elliptical.

Once he understood the planets' motion, he could predict where they would be in the sky in a particular year and month, well into the future. The Ptolemaic system had also been able to make predictions, but its margin of error increased rapidly after just a few years.

In 1629, Kepler used his method to predict that a transit of Mercury across the Sun would take place on December 6, 1631, and Pierre Gassendi was in fact able to observe the planet's transit on the day predicted. Kepler was accurate to within 13′ of longitude, 1′ 05″ of latitude, and 5 hours, 49 minutes, and 30 seconds in time. This observation had made it possible to determine the heliocentric longitude of one of the inferior planets for the very first time.

OBSERVING TRANSITS

In order to watch Mercury or Venus passing in front of the Sun's disk, you must set up your instrument exactly as you would for observing the Sun itself. Mercury is a very small object, and will show up like a perfectly round sunspot, with no penumbra. It will move across the face of the Sun in the course of a few minutes. It is worth remembering that, since Mercury is such a difficult planet to find in normal circumstances, these transits can be a good opportunity to observe it.

A transit of Venus follows much the same pattern, but since Venus has an atmosphere which diffuses the Sun's light, a slight illumination of its far edge can be seen just as it begins to eat into the Sun's disk.

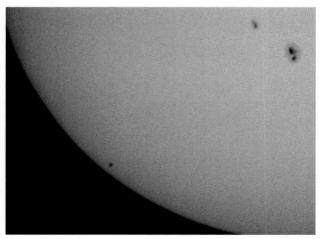

△ *Mercury in transit, 1993 (near lower left edge of Sun).*

LUNAR TRANSIENT PHENOMENA

DESCRIPTION

Though it is a "dead" world, the Moon still has a few surprises to offer. A number of astronomers have noticed a sudden veiling of this or that lunar region by a kind of mist, or a change in color. This kind of event generally lasts only for a few seconds, or minutes at the most.

Even today, we do not fully understand these strange transient phenomena. The most likely explanations are meteorites striking the Moon's surface, or the occasional venting of bubbles of gas through cracks in the surface. Volcanic activity at the Moon's surface ended around 3,000 million years ago, but it is possible that pockets of magma persist beneath the surface and cause these lunar

△ The Crater Alphonsus, very near the center of the Moon's disk, is one place where lunar transient phenomena have been seen.

transient phenomena (LTPs). Seismographs left on the Moon by the Apollo astronauts have recorded only negligible movement, most of it thought to result from seismic activity some 100 kilometers below the surface. (These "moonquakes" are caused by tidal flexing of the Moon.) Although none of the astronauts visiting the Moon between 1969 and 1972 ever detected any such phenomenon, during this period detectors did reveal emissions of radon (a rare gas) near the Crater Aristarchus and some of the meteorite basins. A sudden venting of gas and dust might well cause the sort of temporary veiling of some regions noticed by several observers. But even if these events are really occurring, they are not frequent, so we may have to wait many more years before we can be certain of their cause.

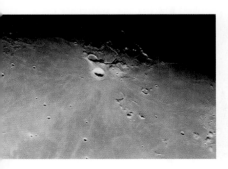

HISTORY AND DISCOVERIES

The first clear references to lunar transient phenomena by astronomers date from

◁ The Crater Aristarchus and the neighboring Schröter Valley, one of the areas where lunar transient phenomena most often occur.

The Crater Plato, recognizable in the Mare Imbrium by its dark, flat bottom. A number of LTPs have been observed here. ▷

the nineteenth century. At that time, many observers were convinced that some features of the lunar topography had actually changed: the most famous case was that of the Crater Messier in the Mare Fecunditatis. Many sketches were drawn, showing what looked like a crumbling of its ramparts, but in fact changes of this kind are due to variations in lighting from the Sun combined with the lunar librations (which alter the appearance of relief features by showing them at different angles). Some of this eyewitness evidence no doubt concerns what we today call lunar transient phenomena. The number of accounts by astronomers of transitory events on the Moon's surface now totals over 1,200. On November 3, 1958, the Russian astrophysicist Nikolai Kozyrev managed to get a spectrum of light from a reddish patch that appeared near the central peak of the Crater Alphonsus, but there is no general agreement that the information he gathered confirms the theory of a volcanic cause.

OBSERVING LUNAR TRANSIENT PHENOMENA

Since these events may occur at any time, there is no particular strategy for observing them, especially as they are very rare. Nevertheless, astronomers have noticed that they tend to happen more frequently in some areas of the Moon than in others. Some 300 events have been observed around the Crater Aristarchus, 70 near the Crater Plato and 25 in the region of the Crater Alphonsus. The edges of some circular seas, such as the Mare Crisium, also seem likely candidates.

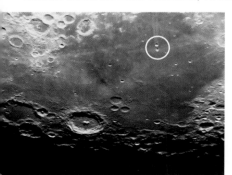

◁ *The Crater Messier puzzled astronomers for a long time, but in fact "changes" in its appearance were merely due to variations in lighting.*

SUPERNOVAE

DESCRIPTION

A supernova is the explosion of a very massive star, a cataclysmic event that marks the death of a star eight or more times the mass of the Sun. Inside all stars, as in the Sun (see p.82), hydrogen is being turned into helium by fusion. In these massive stars, however, the fusion reactions continue beyond this point, producing heavier and heavier elements until iron is formed. A star of 25 to 30 solar masses takes only 8 to 10 million years to "burn" its hydrogen (whereas the Sun will take 10,000 million years to do so). After that, the helium core contracts, causing the hydrogen remaining in its envelope to undergo fusion: the envelope expands, turning the star into a red supergiant. The contraction of the helium core raises its temperature to the point where the helium fuses into carbon and oxygen, over a period of about 500,000 years. At 800 million degrees

Before   *After*

△ *The explosion of Supernova 1987A in the Large Magellanic Cloud, February 1987.*

Celsius, the carbon and oxygen nuclei fuse into neon and sodium: this takes only a few decades. The process speeds up, and the contraction continues until the temperature reaches 1,000 million degrees. The neon lasts only a year, and the oxygen fuses to become silicon in just 15 days. At 3,500 million degrees, the silicon fuses within a single day into iron, the most stable element of all in nature. At that stage, by physical processes which there is no room to describe here, the star's core – which has about the same volume as the Earth – collapses suddenly, no longer able to sustain its own mass. In a fraction of a second, it becomes a sphere just 30 kilometers across, made up entirely of neutrons and so dense that a matchbox full of its matter would weigh more than 1,000 million tonnes.

Supernova 1987A, seen in close-up, two years after the explosion. The ring surrounding it is due to radiation emitted during the explosion reaching layers of gas thrown off much earlier, and causing them to shine. The matter ejected by the supernova event itself is still spread over too small an area to be seen. ▷

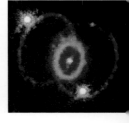

This final gravitational collapse is so sudden that the rest of the star rebounds and is thrown off into space in a gigantic explosion: this is the supernova. The observer sees a rapid increase in the star's luminosity over a number of days, followed by a slow dimming over several years. All this matter hurled into space forms an expanding cloud, with nothing at its center but the small, extremely dense neutron star, or pulsar.

HISTORY AND DISCOVERIES

One of the first supernovae mentioned in history was that of July 4, 1054. Chinese astronomers noticed it in the constellation Taurus, reaching a magnitude that was probably in the region of –5: it could be seen even during the day. The expanding remnants of this supernova can still be obser-

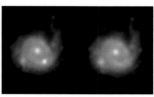

△ *A supernova exploding in another galaxy.*

ved by amateur astronomers today: they form the Crab Nebula, M1 (p.173). With powerful telescopes it has even been possible to detect the pulsar that remains at the nebula's center. Other supernovae have been observed since, the best known being those witnessed by Tycho Brahe in 1574 and Johannes Kepler in 1604. The phenomenon could not be explained, however, until the early twentieth century.

OBSERVING SUPERNOVAE

To observe a supernova with the naked eye is the dream of every astronomer, amateur or professional, but it is unlikely to come true. The exploding star would have to be in the Milky Way or in one of the Magellanic Clouds (which, unfortunately, cannot be seen from northern latitudes). Astrophysicists estimate that somewhere between one and four supernovae can be expected every century in our Galaxy alone, but most of these events will be hidden from us by the thick clouds of gas and dust that block our view of the Galactic equator. As a consequence, only five seem to have been observed in the Milky Way over the last thousand years, an average of one every 200 years. The explosion of one of these massive stars can take place anywhere in the sky, at any time. Astronomers know, of course, which types of star are likely to end their lives in this way: there is no point in waiting for Sirius or Vega to explode, for that is not how stars of their kind are destined to end. On the other hand, some of the brightest stars in the sky could provide us with a supernova at any moment: they include Antares in Scorpius and Betelgeuse in Orion. If one of these explodes, it will light up the night sky and will be visible even during the daytime. Witnessing a supernova in the Milky Way is entirely a matter of patience and sheer luck. It is true that some are spotted in other galaxies every year, even by amateurs – but looking for them requires high-performance equipment, such as a CCD camera.

VARIABLE STARS

DESCRIPTION

There are several different reasons why the brightness of some stars varies. One is that an ordinary star is regularly eclipsed by another, fainter star revolving around it. This is therefore a double star, but one whose components are so close that they cannot be seen separately, even in the most powerful telescopes. These systems are known as eclipsing binaries, and the most famous of them is Algol (in the constellation Perseus): every 2 days and 13 hours, Algol goes from magnitude 2 to magnitude 3.5 in the course of 2 hours 30 minutes. The variation can be detected with the naked eye.

Another cause of a star's variation in brightness is that it pulsates, meaning that it expands and contracts over a fixed period. Some of these stars, such as the Cepheid variables, have periods of variation ranging up to 75 days, and their magnitude changes by no more than 1.7. Others, such as the RR Lyrae variables, have periods of less than one day, with similar amounts (amplitudes) of change. There are pulsating variables with even shorter periods, of the order of a few hours. However, as well as being few in number, they are so faint (the brightest is magnitude 10) that they cannot be observed with the naked eye. The most easily observed variables are those of the same type as Mira in the constellation Cetus. These can change by as much as 7 magnitudes, over periods

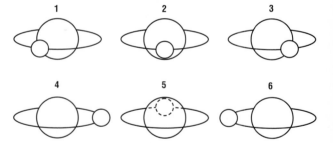

△ ▽ Diagrams illustrating the behavior of an eclipsing binary (Algol type).

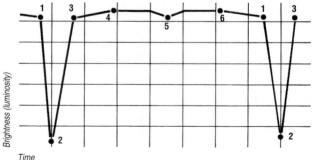

246

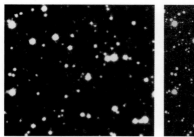

△ *Variation in the brightness of the Musca nova in 1991.*

from 75 to 1,000 days; they are known as Mira stars, or long-period variables. Finally, there are pulsating variables which have no fixed period, but vary irregularly by up to 2 magnitudes.

A third cause of major luminosity changes is stellar eruptions: these are referred to as eruptive variables or novae. They are white dwarfs in a multiple star system which are stealing material from their companions. The accumulation of matter causes them to heat up until a fusion reaction occurs; a huge quantity of matter is thrown off, with an extraordinarily bright flash (10,000 to 100,000 times as bright as the original star). The flash looks to the observer like a new star in the sky, hence the name "stella nova" (literally, "new star"). If matter accumulates again in the same way, there may be another flash years or decades later: these are recurrent novae.

HISTORY AND DISCOVERIES

Around A.D. 1600, a star appeared in the sky where there had been none before, and people spoke of the "stella nova." However, the new arrival only lasted a few days, and then disappeared. For a long time, the term was used for what we now call supernovae, as well as for novae. In 1934, Fritz Zwicky and Walter Baade discovered that these are two different phenomena, and showed that novae are not in fact new stars, but existing stars that suddenly get noticed because of an increase in their brightness.

OBSERVING NOVAE AND VARIABLES

Like looking for supernovae, nova hunting is a game of chance. However, it is helpful to know that they tend to appear in the region of the Galactic equator. As for other types of variable star, professional astronomers know of several thousand, only a few of which are mentioned in this book. All the observatories in the world cannot keep track of every single one, so this is an area where amateur observers can be of use to the professionals. There are a number of variable star observer associations, often working in collaboration with observatories. The AAVSO, for example, has an Internet site at http://www.aavso.org.

GLOSSARY

Accretion: the gravitational capture of matter by a compact, massive body.

Asteroid: a small, irregularly-shaped planet. Most asteroids are found in the region between Mars and Jupiter.

CCD (charge coupled device): a type of electronic detector that is increasingly replacing photographic film in the recording of images of the sky through telescopes.

Cepheid (variable): generic name for a class of variable stars whose prototype is a star in the northern constellation Cepheus. Cepheids characteristically vary in brightness over a fixed period. They have played an important role in the advance of astronomy, by providing a benchmark against which distances between galaxies can be measured.

Chromosphere: the lowest layer of the Sun's atmosphere, consisting of tenuous gas at a temperature of 10,000°C and extending to a height of many thousands of kilometers.

Constellations: conventional groupings of bright stars that form patterns in the sky. Today, 88 constellations are recognized, occupying "territories" which together account for the whole sky.

Convective layer: an outer layer of the Sun, in which heat is transported from the interior to the exterior by convection currents.

Corona: the outer layer of the Sun's atmosphere, even less dense than the chromosphere and reaching temperatures of over 1,000,000°C. It can only be seen during a total eclipse.

Declination: the angular distance, north or south, of an object with respect to the celestial equator (the equivalent of latitude on Earth).

Diffraction: the way in which light rays from a point source are bent from their straight path as they encounter the edge of an opaque obstacle.

Ecliptic: the plane in which the Earth orbits the Sun. As seen from Earth, the ecliptic is represented by the apparent path which the Sun traces across the sky in the course of a year.

Expansion of the Universe: the general movement of the galaxies away from one another, as if the universe were growing in volume. This expansion, first observed by Edwin Hubble, began with the primordial explosion of the Big Bang, some 13,000 million years ago.

Eyepiece: part of an optical instrument, consisting of two or more lenses, placed at the focus of the instrument in order to obtain an enlarged image.

Focal length: the distance between an astronomical instrument's objective and its focus (the point where the light rays concentrated by it meet).

Galactic equator: a pale streak in the sky, named "Via Lactea" (the Milky Way) in Antiquity. It is the plane in which most of the Galaxy's stars lie.

Galaxy: a gigantic group of stars. All the stars in the universe are grouped in galaxies, either irregularly shaped or in the form of spiral disks. Each galaxy contains thousands of millions of stars.

Granule: an irregularly shaped cellular structure, 1,000–1,500 kilometers across, formed by convection at the Sun's surface.

Jovian: belonging to or similar in type to the planet Jupiter.

Libration: the apparent slight wobble of a body (in particular, the Moon) upon its axis.

Light year (ly): a unit of distance, equivalent to the distance traveled by light in one year. As light travels at around 186,000 miles or 300,000 kilometers per second, one light year is approximately 5,870,000 million miles, or 9,460,000 million kilometers.

Magnitude: the apparent brightness of a heavenly body, expressed as a number. The smaller the number, the greater the brightness.

Meteorite: a solid, rocky body traveling through space, which crashes onto the surface of Earth or of another planet.

Milky Way: our own Galaxy, containing some 100,000 million stars, of which the Sun is one. It is a disk 100,000 light years in diameter and 10,000 light years thick.

Oblateness: the slight flattening at the poles of most planets, which means that they are not exact spheres.

Orbit: the path traced by one body revolving around another, whose satellite it is.

Outgas: to release gas. The ices of which comets are largely composed turn to gas in the heat of the Sun, in a process called "outgassing."

Parsec: a unit of distance, equivalent to the distance from which the radius of the Earth's orbit would appear to extend over 1″ of arc. One parsec equals 3.26 light years.

Perihelion: the point in a planet's or comet's orbit at which it comes closest to the Sun.

Photosphere: the apparent surface (the layer that produces the visible light) of the Sun, or of another star.

Plate tectonics: the mechanism by which the more or less rigid plates forming the Earth's crust move in relation to each other.

Protoplanet: a sizable accumulation of matter which, over the course of several million years, will grow to become a planet.

Right ascension: the celestial coordinate that is the equivalent of longitude on Earth.

Saros: a period of 18 years and 10–11 days, during which 43 solar and the same number of lunar eclipses take place. From this, it can be predicted when eclipses will recur.

Satellite: a body that is kept in orbit round a planet by its gravitational field.

Sidereal day: the time taken by a planet or satellite to rotate once on its own axis with respect to the stars.

Silicates: grains of sand.

Solar System: the system of planets and other bodies orbiting the Sun.

Spectrum: the image obtained by splitting visible light or any other radiation into its components. The best known manifestation of the visible light spectrum is the rainbow.

Supernova: an explosion which ends the life of a very massive star.

Thermonuclear reaction: the fusion of two atoms which takes place at very high temperatures, producing energy.

Trojans: the asteroids orbiting the Sun in more or less the same orbit and with the same period as Jupiter.

Universal time (UT): the time at Greenwich Observatory in England, used as a standard time reference throughout the world, to avoid confusion due to differences in local times.

Year: the time taken by the Earth to complete one circuit around the Sun (365.25 days).

Zodiac: a band of sky extending 8.5° to either side of the ecliptic, the plane in which the planets, the Sun and the Moon are found.

INDEX

Page numbers in **bold** type indicate main entries. Numbers in plain type refer to the text, and those in *italics* to the illustrations (photographs, drawings, diagrams and maps).

PHOTOGRAPHIC CREDITS

t = top; m = middle; b = below

Cover: Fletcher/CIEL & ESPACE (t left), **Fujii/CIEL & ESPACE** (t rt), **NASA/CIEL & ESPACE** (b left), **Brunier/CIEL & ESPACE** (b rt).

AAO/Malin/CIEL & ESPACE: 13, 182, 189 m, 191 b, 203 b, 204 b, 213 b, 214 b, 219 b, 233 t; **Anglaret/CIEL & ESPACE:** 235 t; **Anière/CIEL & ESPACE:** 243 b; **APB/CIEL & ESPACE:** 84; **Arsidi/CIEL & ESPACE:** 242 t; **Birnbaum/CIEL & ESPACE:** 32; **Bourdis/CIEL & ESPACE:** 20, 39 b; **Bret/CIEL & ESPACE:** 12 t, 98; **Brunier/CIEL & ESPACE:** 14, 25, 29, 30–31, 33 t, 33 b, 39 t, 122 t, 239 t left, 239 t rt; **Cannat/CIEL & ESPACE:** 87 b; **CFHT/CIEL & ESPACE:** 150 b, 152 b, 163 b, 167 b; **CIEL & ESPACE:** 24, 46; **Cirou/CIEL & ESPACE:** 34, 36; **Davis/CIEL & ESPACE:** 83; **Delaye/CIEL & ESPACE:** 241; **Devaux/CIEL & ESPACE:** 221 b; **Dionne/CIEL & ESPACE:** 82; **Dragesco/CIEL & ESPACE:** 234, 243 t; **ESA/CIEL & ESPACE:** 133, 232; **ESO/CIEL & ESPACE:** 244 t left, 244 t rt, 247 left, 247 rt; **B & S Fletcher/CIEL & ESPACE:** 132, 154 b, 157 b, 169 b, 173 b, 177 b, 189 b; **Fujii/CIEL & ESPACE:** 8 t rt, 15, 16, 17, 38, 40, 52 b, 56, 58, 60, 62, 64, 66, 68, 70, 130 b, 173 m, 206 b, 226, 228, 230, 237 b; **Graëff/CIEL & ESPACE:** 21, 227, 233 b; **Graëff/NASA/CIEL & ESPACE:** 105 b; **Hale Observatories/CIEL & ESPACE:** 149 b; **Hodasava/CIEL & ESPACE:** 108; **Hodasava/NASA/CIEL & ESPACE:** 72, 89 t, 90; **IAC/RGO/CIEL & ESPACE:** 12 b; **Ichkanian/CIEL & ESPACE:** 242 b; **Iki/CIEL & ESPACE:** 94 t; **Joly/CIEL & ESPACE:** 122 b; **JPL/CIEL & ESPACE:** 6, 93 b, 109; **JPL/Hodasava/CIEL & ESPACE:** 78; **Lecacheux/Colas/S2P:** 101 t, 120 m, 120 b; **Lodriguss/CIEL & ESPACE:** 174 b, 188 b, 208 b; **Lowell Obs./CIEL & ESPACE:** 105 t, 128 b left, 128 b rt; **Manchu/CIEL & ESPACE:** 47, 100–101 b, 131; **Mouillet/Obs. Grenoble/CIEL & ESPACE:** 81; **NASA/CIEL & ESPACE:** 7, 8 b (3 photos), 9 t, 9 b (3 photos), 11, 73, 75, 77, 79, 80, 88–89 b, 91, 94 b, 96–97 b, 99, 102, 103 t, 107 t, 110, 111, 113, 114 t, 114 b, 115 t, 115 b, 116, 117 t, 117 b, 118, 119 t, 120 t, 121, 123 t, 123 b, 125 t, 125 b, 126, 129 t, 129 b, 144 b, 229 b, 239 b, 244 b; **NOAA/CIEL & ESPACE:** 35; **NOAO/CIEL & ESPACE:** 135, 212 b, 245; **Numazawa/CIEL & ESPACE:** 19; **Numazawa/APB/CIEL & ESPACE:** 10 t, 10 b, 37, 237 t; **OMP/CIEL & ESPACE:** 85; **OMP/APB/CIEL & ESPACE:** 84; **Parmegiani/CIEL & ESPACE:** 235 b; **Parviainen/CIEL & ESPACE:** 229 t; **Riffle/CIEL & ESPACE:** 181 b; **Royal Society/CIEL & ESPACE:** 23; **Sac-Peak/Hodasawa/CIEL & ESPACE:** 8 m; **Sauzereau/CIEL & ESPACE:** 86–87 t; **Schild/CIEL & ESPACE:** 148 b; **SIC/CIEL & ESPACE:** 97 t; **Sisk/CIEL & ESPACE:** 134; **USGS/CIEL & ESPACE:** 92, 93 t, 103 b, 104, 124, 127; **Watabe/CIEL & ESPACE:** 41, 52–53 t, 106.